Making Scenes 1

Short Plays for Young Actors

School Journey to the Centre of the Earth by Daisy Campbell with Ken Campbell, **Faith, Hope and Charity** by Ödön von Horváth, translated by Christopher Hampton, **Stone Moon** by Judith Johnson, **The Forest of Mirrors** by Gregory Motton

Making Scenes 1 is an anthology of four short plays for young actors performed across Britain and showcased at the Royal National Theatre in June and July 1995, as part of the BT National Connections festival.

Each play is accompanied by an interview with its author by Jim Mulligan; acting notes and exercises for young actors by Suzy Graham-Adriani, Director/Producer for BT National Connections; and the volume is introduced by Literary Consultant Nick Drake.

BT is proud to sponsor BT National Connections, an Education Project of the Royal National Theatre, providing over 4000 young people with the unique opportunity of working on new plays and translations specially commissioned or selected from a group of recognized playwrights.

It is through projects such as these that BT is able to help bring the enjoyment and benefits of the arts to communities throughout the UK. Rodger Broad, BT's Head of Corporate Sponsorship said, 'It is not often that a company is offered the opportunity to help develop and then sponsor a project that so completely supports its own objectives of "adding to the quality of life in the communities in which it conducts its business". In BT National Connections, we have found the perfect project to do just that.'

Making Scenes 1

Short Plays for Young Actors

School Journey to the Centre of the Earth
Daisy Campbell with Ken Campbell

Faith, Hope and Charity
translated by Christopher Hampton
from the play by Ödön von Horváth

Stone Moon
Judith Johnson

The Forest of Mirrors
Gregory Motton

Introduced by Nick Drake,
with author interviews by Jim Mulligan
and production notes by Suzy Graham-Adriani

Methuen Drama
in association with the Royal National Theatre

Methuen New Theatrescripts
in association with the Royal National Theatre

First published in Great Britain 1995
by Methuen Drama in association with the Royal National Theatre
an imprint of Reed Consumer Books Ltd
Michelin House, 81 Fulham Road, London SW3 6RB
and Auckland, Melbourne, Singapore and Toronto

ISBN 0 413 69840 8

A CIP catalogue record for this book is available from the British Library

Front cover image courtesy of Tony Stone Images

Typeset by Wilmaset Ltd, Birkenhead, Wirral
Printed by Clays Ltd, St Ives plc

Caution

Contents

BT National Connections

The plays, introduced by **Nick Drake**, *the scheme's Literary Consultant*

'As the guardians of public morals warned, youngsters are enacting scenes from Quentin Tarantino's *Pulp Fiction*. However, the results were not the violence that had been predicted. Last week, there were reports of two sixteen-year-old pupils at a comprehensive near Bristol performing the opening "Pumpkin/Honey-Bunny" scenes from *Pulp Fiction* for a mock GCSE drama exam. The two dismissed classical choices such as *Twelfth Night* and *Pygmalion*, and won a borderline A grade for their performance.' *Screen*, March 1995.

There are at least three points to be made from this news item; firstly, there's a hunger for new plays among young actors; secondly, there's a poverty of original plays by exceptional writers available to them; and thirdly, young people are excited by writing which is absolutely contemporary, sophisticated, and preferably heretical in its use of form and language. At the same time, playwrights – especially new playwrights – have found the opportunities for productions of their new work diminishing around the country: most theatres' repertoires are now filled largely with revivals, productions of old plays by long-dead writers, and adaptations of novels.

Suzy Graham-Adriani and the Royal National Theatre had been researching ways of answering these needs, and she and I began to discuss how to turn the situation into a creative opportunity. Put simply, we wanted to create an exciting and innovative repertoire of new plays by important playwrights for young actors to perform principally for audiences of their peers. In March 1994, with the National's backing, we began to ask playwrights whose work we admired if they would be interested in the idea. The plays would be produced not once, but many times in different venues, and with different ideas and interpretations, all around the country; there would be regional festivals at ten partnership theatres, and the whole scheme would culminate with a big festival of ten productions at the Royal National Theatre in London in June and July 1995. Thanks to generous sponsorship from BT, we were able to bring this whole concept to life in a project called 'BT National Connections'.

We explained to the writers that the plays could only be about an hour long, but that otherwise they were free to write about whatever interested them (as they absolutely ought to be), and for as big a cast as they wished. We commissioned six new plays, two translations of interesting and relatively unknown works (one of which – *The Ice Palace* – was adapted from a short Norwegian novel), and included two new plays that had already been written, but which had not had proper productions, and which were then worked on further by the writers. And I found two older, but remarkable and little-known plays; this made up a portfolio of twelve.

The writers began work in the spring of 1994, and produced first drafts that September. The first reading of these drafts was incredibly exciting; brand new work from important writers. Each play was unexpected, original and above all a work of the imagination; vivid language, big stories, fascinating characters; in each there was a various, and large-hearted sense that the world was bigger and stranger than you had thought. There were plays set in difficult urban worlds, in a clearing in a wood, in a remote village in winter; plays about love, about freedom, and above all about journeys. And however obliquely, they all discovered original theatrical ways of looking at the world *now*.

The plays were completed in November and early December 1994. We circulated descriptions of the writers and the plays to all the groups involved in the scheme, and then invited representatives of each group to come to the National for a day of workshops with the writers on their plays, led by accomplished directors of new writing. As I write this, there are one hundred and fifty productions of these plays in rehearsal in every part of the land. And the publication of the plays in these volumes means that they are now available to anyone, to discover for themselves. They constitute the first plays in a new repertoire of new writing.

The Plays: Volume One

Ödön von Horváth's *Faith, Hope and Charity*, translated by Christopher Hampton, is subtitled 'a little dance of death in five acts'. The quizzical discrimination and wry coolness of this phrase suggest some of the qualities of von Horváth's writing: sharp, bleak, ironic, unsweetened; also, particularly, a sense of the miniature scale and zig-zag farce of human suffering, set against a social panorama of futility. Von Horváth described this as his dramatic arena: 'the gigantic struggle of the individual and society, this eternal battle with no peaceful outcome.' The play takes the desiccated facts of an actual case of judicial error, and dramatises them in sharp fragments of scenes set within a remarkably contained and tightly-constructed arc of actions, to create a modern tragedy. The dramatic landscape of a disintegrating and heartless city in which survival is hard, and barely moral, is instantly recognisable as the ubiquitous urban setting of our century. So is the imagery of a tattered social fabric; queues of the hopeless at the gates of institutions, people barely surviving on the streets, casualties whose plight is casually ignored; here Faith, Hope and Charity are nowhere to be found.

The first scene of Gregory Motton's *The Forest of Mirrors* tells the play's 'story': 'King Cnut is just about to get married, and well, you know what love is, the bride ran off and left him for this monster who lived on a rock in the sea . . . but along comes Fitz the Faithful and another man quite like himself called Fitz the Unfaithful . . . who helped him with a job to go and fetch the missing bride.' But this is just the beginning, for the real story is the twists and turns, the quirks, crimes and glories, of the heart, and the mysteries of human nature's need and gift for the 'inspiration of love' (as the Girl puts it), and its fear of loneliness. The play opens with an image for all of this; a man beating at his own front door to be admitted. And it closes with an equally powerful scene in which Fitz the Unfaithful, seeking the release of death, finds a Young Woman who has just fallen in love 'for the sake of her soul'. It borrows some of the elements and conventions of fairy stories (kings, monsters, quests and beheadings) and uses dramatically some of their associative, zig-zag dream-methods too; enigmatic events and imaginative impossibilities in which the world stops making sense – and seems the truer for it. It also draws on the modern world of shopping centres, hatcheck girls and TV. But it is above all a play about the inexplicable heart, and as such takes us beneath the appearance of things into that ambiguous realm, the Forest of Mirrors itself.

Judith Johnson's *Stone Moon* has a different kind of epic arc to its story, and an epic scale too; it is written for a large cast, which can comprise exclusively women, and is set mostly in a village square and a stone quarry – both large-scale, open dramatic spaces. The play embraces large social themes of repression and freedom, but it is above all about love. The gangs of women who work the stone quarry have to deny the need for love, because they see that love leads to sex, childbirth and to loss of emotional and economic independence. But such deprivation, rigidly adhered to, has its own emotional consequences; Kiri, a free spirit who cannot suppress the truth of her feelings, is determined not to be a victim of circumstance or of fate, but wants the freedom to explore, discover and celebrate love. This brings her into conflict with her society and its taboos, and into frightening contact with its haunting spirits, especially her grandmother's broken-hearted ghost. Finally events force her to discover for herself a more difficult and courageous way forward in her quest to create the terms of her own life in a world that represses that freedom.

School Journey to the Centre of the Earth by Daisy Campbell with Ken Campbell is something completely different. Written for younger performers, and with a fine, energetic, improvised quality to the characters, it is a comic and feisty account of a group of schoolchildren managing to reimagine their day-trip to Alton Towers as something stranger than anything Jules Verne, that master of science fantasy, ever described. Tricia leads the way in the fantasy, and in her we meet a great Walter Mitty character with a compulsive and amazing ability to reimagine, embellish and exaggerate the facts into stories so tall they are almost believable. Along the way the group argue and speculate frankly about death, love, sex, zits, video nasties, and the science of life underground; perfectly reasonable questions – such as: is Miss Sheehan a Russian spy? and is the Corkscrew ride at Alton Towers possibly the entrance to the tunnel that leads to the centre of the Earth? – turn out to have some perfectly weird and wonderful answers.

March 1995

School Journey to the Centre of the Earth

Daisy Campbell
with Ken Campbell

Characters

Stacey	eight-and-three-quarters
Georgia	nine next Tuesday
Chrissy	same as Stacey
Richard	nine last week
Hal	nine in two weeks
Tricia	eight-and-three-quarters-and-a-bit
Sonny	eight-and-a-quarter
Anna	nine in twenty-one days
James	just nine, wears 'well-in' trainers
Rab	nine-and-a-bit, also wears 'well-in' trainers
William	ten in three weeks
Jonathan	eight-and-a-half
Louise	eight
Ben	eight-and-a-half, he is like an old man. He wears cords and a grey cardigan. He has asthma and is consequently a little wheezy. He sucks a pencil as he talks as if it were a pipe
Matthew	nearly nine
Tom	nine in October, Clarks shoes, Snoopy lunch-box
Emma	unknown

The children are all dressed in every-day clothes.

Coach. Children singing football songs, one of which is to the tune of 'Glory, Glory Hallelujah'.

Stacey   That ain't fair, Georgia. You promised me three weeks ago that I could sit next to you on the bus.

Georgia   Yeah, but I promised Chrissy four weeks ago.

Anna   (*to* **Tricia**) See *Neighbours* yesterday?

Tricia   Yeah.

Anna   I can't believe we're gonna miss it today – both times. Bouncer is about to be run over.

Tricia   There might be tellys at Alton Towers.

Rab   (*butting in*) Or we could arrange for the driver to run over a dog on the way, then it'll be like bringing *Neighbours* right to yer doorstep!

Anna   That's not even funny. Dogs have feelings, you know. It's not like in *Neighbours* where it's made up. They don't really kill Bouncer in *Neighbours*, you know. It's made up.

Hal   (*To* **Tricia**) I'm having the window seat.

Tricia   Bloody not.

Hal   Soddin' am.

A large crowd of boys burst suddenly through the crowd, screaming;

The boys   Back of the bus! Back of the bus!

On hearing this, all the kids make a wild dash for the back of the bus.

Everyone more or less settled, after a large fight at the back of the bus – **James, Rab, Louise** *and* **Richard** *having won – the register is taken.*

Sonny   Yes, Miss Sheehan.

Anna   Yes, Miss.

Miss Sheehan speaks. She is invisible to the audience, but to the children she is very real.

Tricia   (*making spastic noises*) James!

James   What? Oh, yes Miss.

Miss Sheehan speaks.

What? Oh, yes Miss *Sheehan*.

Hal   Tottenham beat Arsenal 2–0.

Rab   (*mimicking* **William**) Here, Miss Sheehan.

Jonathan   (*loudly*) Yes, Miss Sheehan!

Tricia   (*even louder*) Yes, Miss Sheehan.

It is now apparent that this is a game. The one who can answer in the loudest voice wins.

William   Here, Miss.

Richard   (*louder*) Here, Miss.

Louise   (*almost screaming*) Yes, Miss!

Ben   (*quietly, self-consciously*) Yes, Miss Sheehan.

The Kids   (*making spastic noises*) Mr Bean! Mr Bean!

A small boy gets on the coach and looks for a space. Despite the abundance of free seats, they all appear to be saved.

James   You're late, Tom.

The register is still going on in the background.

Matthew   (*as* **Tom** *attempts to sit down*) Sorry saved.

Chrissy   Sorry saved.

Many are still waving goodbye to their parents through the windows, but are beginning to tire of this activity and are chatting to friends at the same time.

Rab   Sorry. This is a Clark's shoe free zone.

Miss Sheehan speaks. **Rab***'s face falls.*

Tom   Thank you, Miss. (*He sits.*)

Rab   Miss, I'm charging you with the doctor's bill when we all catch the Lurgi.

James   (*to* **Rab**) We'd better eject Lurgis.

Rab *and* **James** *touch their heads, then cross their arms to touch their shoulders then touch their waists.*

Rab ⎫
James ⎬   Lurgis ejected for life!

Miss Sheehan speaks.

Everyone   (*while holding up see-through plastic bags*) Yes, Miss.

Georgia   Can't we get the paper sort, Miss? These sort are disgustin'. If anyone's sick you can see right through them.

Jonathan   The paper ones are worse though. If you're sick in those, they go all soggy at the bottom and burst.

Georgia   Thanks for that, John.

Anna   Oh. Miss. I've left my pack-lunch in the classroom. Can I go and get it?

James   No, you can starve.

Anna   Thanks, Miss. (*She leaves.*)

Ben   Are we ever going to get going?

Rab   He speaks. Quiet please, everybody. Mr Bean has something he wishes to share. What was it? Mr Bean?

Ben   Er . . . no . . . I was just . . . It doesn't matter.

The electronic sound of a 'Gameboy' becomes audible. It is traced to **Louise**. *Everyone in the surrounding seats leans in, intent on seeing how badly she's doing.*

Richard   (*spastic noises*) You're supposed to headbut it, and *then* the mushroom comes out.

Louise   (*sarcastically*) You don't say?

Rab   Jump! Jump! Ah. You missed it.

Stacey   I'm feelin' car sick.

Jonathan   We haven't even set off yet.

Chrissy   Excuse me, Miss. But it ain't fair the way that Emma and Matthew have both got whole rows to themselves. They can stretch out properly.

Miss Sheehan speaks.

Chrissy   No, but I'd rather be able to stretch out than have someone to talk to.

Matthew *is hauled across by Miss to sit with* **Emma**.

Matthew   No. Miss. That ain't fair. I got here first and taxed the whole row.

Stacey   You're not allowed to tax the whole row. You're only allowed to tax one seat. And one for a friend.

Matthew   I'm not sitting next to her. No way.

Miss Sheehan speaks.

Alright, Miss. But if she so much as wipes one bogie on me then you're payin' the cleanin' bill.

Emma *has not batted an eyelid throughout this exchange.*

James   Can we go now? At this rate we'll have time for one go on the Corkscrew and have to leave.

The coach revs up, and from the movement of the children and the frantic waving out of the back window, it is obvious that their journey has begun.

The lights fade and come up on only three seats of the coach. **Tricia, Sonny** *and* **Hal. Tricia** *is still waving frantically out of the back window.*

Tricia   Bye Mum. Mummy – (*Cries.*) I'm homesick. I'm not cryin' I'm not. Anyway, (*To* **Hal**.) don't diss me. You're not in the gang. Me and Sonny are best mates. We tell each other everything. Everything. You wouldn't believe some of the stuff that Sonny's told me.

Tricia *suddenly appears far more pally with* **Hal** *than with* **Sonny. Sonny** *looks left out. He grabs* **Tricia***'s arm.*

Sonny   You say anything, I'll never speak to you ever again.

Tricia   Some stuff that he gets up to. Urrgh. It's disgustin'.

Sonny   I'll break your legs.

Hal   Like what?

Tricia   You'd be sick if I was to tell you.

Hal   No.

Sonny *is on the floor attempting to break one of* **Tricia***'s legs. He resembles a dog rubbing up and down someone's leg.*

Hal   That sort of thing? (*Indicating the grunting* **Sonny**.)

Tricia   Yeah. Just like that. He has these funny turns, see. I just let him get on with it.

Hal   What sort of secrets 'as he told you?

Tricia   I'm sworn to secrecy.

Hal   Yeah, obviously. What are they?

Sonny   I'll break your neck!

Tricia   Well. Don't say that I told you, but Sonny well fancies you.

Sonny   (*suddenly sitting back in his seat*) That's not . . . you said . . . you weren't gonna tell . . . anyways, it's not true anyway.

Tricia   You fancy her.

Sonny   I don't. In fact I hate her.

Tricia   (*singing*) Sonny and Halina up a tree. K-I-S-S-I-N-G!

Sonny   I'm never talkin' to you ever again.

Tricia   Hold hands! Hold hands!

Sonny   Leave me alone.

Tricia   You two are gonna get married.

Hal   I don't fink so.

Sonny   I'm never talkin' to you ever again.

Tricia   Oh, Sonny. You're my best friend.

Sonny   Oh, alright.

Hal   Anyway, Simon might get jealous.

Tricia   Who's Simon?

Sonny   The pieman.

Small, half-hearted laugh from **Tricia** *and* **Hal**, *referring to* **Sonny**'s *unsuccessful joke.*

Tricia   That's rubbish.

Hal   That's so sad.

Tricia   Yeah, so sad.

Hal   He's my boy-friend.

Tricia   How old is he anyway?

Sonny   Yeah?

Hal   He's thirteen.

Tricia   THIRTEEN?!!

Sonny   Older boys are stupid.

Hal   Older boys are the best.

Sonny   They only want you for one thing.

Tricia   That's like your dad though!

Hal   What do they want me for?

Sonny   Well. They only want you for one thing. Like, that thing could be anything, but, thing is, they only want you for that and not for nothing else. My uncle's older than my aunt and she said that's true. That he only wants her for one thing. She said it to my mum. I reckon it's her cooking.

Tricia   She good?

Sonny   Yeah, she makes this well nice ice-cream cake. She made one for my eighth birthday. Well yummy it was. But she is fat. Like really fat. She's one of those people you can't imagine on the loo.

Tricia   Yeah, cos like if they sat on the loo, all their flab would bulge over the edges and touch the floor either side.

Hal   You are so immature.

Tricia   Am not. What's that?

Hal   It's when you're younger.

Sonny   Just 'cos you've got an older boy-friend.

Tricia   Look, I am eight-and-three-quarters and I am almost nine.

Hal   I'm nine next week.

Tricia   Well, I'm nine last week. I'm eleven. I'm fifteen. I'm fourteen. I'm seventeen. I work in Sue Ryder. I'm married.

Hal   Shut . . .

Tricia   I'm married to this bloke on the telly.

Sonny   What's his name?

Tricia   He's in *Neighbours*.

Hal   Which one?

Tricia   He's Brad off *Neighbours*.

Hal   What, so you're Mrs Willis?

Tricia   Yeah.

Hal   But you're not. Oh deee-aaar. You got shamed. Gutted.

Tricia   I am.

Hal   No. You're called Tricia Park. So you lied. Liar, liar. Pants on fire.

Tricia   No, but you see, 'cos you're not 'sposed to get married until you're a grown-up, I have to have a fake name, 'cos I've got married before I should and if the police found out they'd hang me.

Sonny   Don't be stupid. They don't have the death penalty any more.

Tricia   Yeah, they do. But only for treason and getting married to Australians when you're too young.

Sonny   Oh. What's treason?

Tricia   It's cussin' down the Royal Family.

James   (*popping up*) Who guffed?

Hal   Sonny, do you really fancy me?

Sonny   Not since you've got a boy-friend.

Hal   I reckon *you two* should get married.

Tricia   We already are.

James's voice   Who ate egg this morning?

Hal   You're married? When?

Tricia   Yesterday. (*Whispering.*) Just pretend.

Sonny   No. We're not.

Tricia   Oh. Shut up. You've ruined it. She believed me as well.

Suddenly the smell of the fart reaches **Tricia, Hal** *and* **Sonny**. *They pull their tops over their noses.*

Sonny   (*through his shirt*) I'm sick of you goin' around tellin' everyone we're married. We're not. Alright?

Tricia   Are too.

Sonny   Am not.

Tricia   Are too.

Sonny   Am not.

James   (*leaning over from behind*) Shut up, will yer?

Tricia   Look, we're havin' a lover's tiff. Alright?

Sonny   Am not.

Tricia   Are too. Are too. Are too. (*Covering her ears with her hands.*) Din din din din din din. I'm not listening. I'm not listening. Din din din. I can't hear you. Din infinity. Din infinity!

A hand reaches through the seating, from behind, and tries to hit **Tricia**. *Failing that, it hits* **Sonny** *and pulls* **Tricia**'*s hair.*

Tricia   You don't love me anymore. Anyway, I don't care 'cos I fancy that one over there.

Hal   Which one?

It's now obvious **Tricia** *is actually pointing through the window.*

Tricia   The one over there, yeah. But not the one with the beard. The other one.

Hal   Oi, mister! She fancies you. My friend fancies you.

Tricia   No don't. Don't say anything. I'm so embarrassed. I can't beleeeve it.

Sonny   I know him.

Hal   No you don't.

Sonny   Yes I do. He smells. He smells of piss.

Tricia   He smells of piss. (*Pause.*) Urrgh. That's disgusting.

Sonny   Shut up. You told me the other day that you wet the bed and your mum got really cross and told you off.

James   (*popping up*) Waaaah. He got yer. Darked. Gutted. Shamed. Shamed big time.

Rab   (*popping up*) Waaah. Gutted. (*To* **James**.) What happened?

James   She wets the bed.

Rab   Shame.

Tricia   I didn't. That's not . . . It wasn't me.

Rab   It wasn't you? What, so someone's been crawlin' into your bed at night, pissin' and then crawlin' out again?

Tricia   I spilled a glass of water, alright.

Sarcastic, sympathetic nods.

Hal   Oh yeah?

Sonny   An' I feel sorry for your sister who has to sleep in the same bed.

Hal   Urrgh.

James   Lesbos.

Tricia   That is a lie. My sister . . . I haven't got a sister.

Sonny   Yes you do.

Tricia   Alright. But she doesn't sleep in the same bed. We've got bunk-beds, and I get the top one 'cos I'm good.

Rab   So it must drip through.

Hal   Urrgh.

Tricia   I don't wet the bed. I don't wet the bed. I'm not listening. (*Hands over ears.*) Din din din. I'm not listening.

Sonny   I wouldn't sleep with you.

Pause.

I mean, in a bed.

Tricia   I'm going to the toilet. (*At* **Sonny** – *mouthing it.*) I hate you.

Rab   Yeah, we wouldn't want you doin' it on your seat.

James   'Praps you should sleep on the toilet. That would solve all your problems.

James *leaps over his seat, plopping into* **Tricia**'s *seat.*

James   Sorry Miss – There's a spider on *my* seat.

Rab   Sorry Miss. (*He sits down.*)

James   (*to* **Sonny**) You've got a zit on your chin.

Hal   Yeah; I noticed that.

Sonny   (*becoming really self-conscious*) Oh, have I? Oh, right . . . I

James   Don't worry. It's not that big. Tomorrow it'll be all yellow on top and you can pop it.

Sonny   Oh, right. Thanks.

James   You're quite fat. I hadn't noticed before. Looks like you're havin' a baby.

Hal   Yeah.

Sonny   But I can't 'cos I'm a boy.

James   Did I say that? No. I said you *look* like you're havin' a baby.

Rab   Miss, how long is it 'til we get there?

Miss Sheehan speaks.

Rab   That's no good. I can't sit on this bloody coach – I mean, silly coach – much longer. An' by the time we get there, I'll be too coach sick to go on the Corkscrew.

Hal   Have you been on the one at Alton Towers?

Rab   No, but I been on the one at Chessington.

Louise   (*leaning in*) I've been on that one! It's wicked, innit?

Rab   Yeah. I love that bit, you know, when you're slowly goin' up and then . . .

Louise   Oh yeah, an' then you, like wait at the top for, like, ages . . .

Rab   It's only a couple of seconds . . .

Louise   Yeah, but it feels like . . .

Rab   Yeah, it feels like ages. And then suddenly it dips and . . .

Louise   Yeah, an' your tummy gets left behind.

Rab   Yeah, your tummy. An' then before you know it you're goin' . . .

Both have begun to live the ride and, as their audience watches, they too begin to swerve and lurch with **Rab** *and* **Louise***.*

Louise   On the upside-down bit . . .

Rab   An' you're 'Waaaah!' and 'Ooooo!'

Louise   An' then you turn the corner an' . . .

Rab   You think you're gonna come off the rails and 'Weeee!' and 'Aaaaarrghh!'

Hal   Woooh!

James   Aaaaah!

Georgia   Excellaaaant!

Ben   Help!

Richard   And then it's the end of the ride.

Rab   Shut up. We haven't got to the best bit yet.

Louise   So you start to climb up again . . .

Everyone is leaning back as they climb the second loop.

Rab   An' now we're right upside down . . .

Louise   An' we stop for a couple of seconds . . .

Rab   Yeah, you stop right upside down . . .

The children all appear to be hanging upside down. Suddenly there is a complete silence – a long pause while they hang.

Rab   And then –

Everyone lurches forward and hurtles down the second loop, a look of terror on their faces.

Georgia   Help!

Anna   I want to get off!

Louise   An' we're goin' round that corner . . .

Chrissy   Wicked!

Sonny   Can I open my eyes yet?

Stacey   I'm gonna die! I'm gonna die!

Georgia   I hate it! I hate it!

They lurch to the side as they go round a sharp bend.

Rab   An' we're comin' to the end . . . (*They are all thrown forward as the ride stops. They pant heavily.*) What do you think?

Tom   (*breathless*) That's excellent.

Long pause.

Tricia   (*returning*) Out.

James   Talk about take yer time on the bog. That bog's for everyone you know. Not just for people with pissing problems.

Tricia   Get out of my seat.

James   Urrgh. Yours is it? I thought it felt a bit damp.

Tricia   If you ain't careful I'll piss on you.

James   Wow. You've been on the bog all that time and you've still got enough wee left to piss on me? You're amazing, Trish. I've gotta say. You're world class pisser of the year.

Tricia   You think you're so cool.

James   Yep.

Tricia   Well, you're not. (*Shouting.*) Hands up who thinks James is cool.

Rab *shoots his hand up. After a glare from* **James**, *so does* **Sonny**. **Hal** *has her hand sort of half way.* **James** *doesn't even look to see who's on his side.*

Tricia   See? Three.

James   No one else heard you. And anyway, I'm not gonna even ask anyone what they think of you, 'cos you'd be so upset that you'd throw yourself off the coach. And you're so fat that you'd go right through the world and come out at Australia.

Tricia   No.

James   You would.

Ben   Actually, she wouldn't.

Tricia   Thanks, Mr Bean.

Ben   Yes, even weighing 950 thousand, billion, zillion tonnes . . .

Tricia   (*hits* **Ben**) Thanks a lot.

Ben   No no. Just supposing. Well, even then, due to gravity, the furthest Tricia could possibly fall would be to the centre of the Earth.

Tricia   Yeah.

James   Well, you'd fall there then.

Tricia   Gladly. Anything to get away from you. Anyway, it's brilliant down there. I've been.

James   Crap.

Jonathan   So've I.

Tricia   Yeah, what's it like then?

Jonathan   Well, you go down this tunnel which is in . . . urm . . . in Staf . . . ford . . . shire.

Georgia   That's where we're going, isn't it?

Tricia   Yeah, see, I'm not actually supposed to tell you this but we're not actually going to Alton Towers at all.

Anna   What?

Tricia   We are actually going to the centre of the Earth.

Georgia   (*sarcastically*) Yeah, right.

Tricia   No, it's true. Ask my granny. Ask my turtle. We're on a mission but we don't know it. At least yous lot don't know it. What I'm gonna tell you is very dangerous information. In fact, it's probably best that I don't tell you.

Anna   No, tell.

Tricia Well, I suppose if I tell you what's going on you might be more prepared. We're bein' used as guinea pigs. They want to see if it's possible to live down there.

Anna They?

Tricia (*whispering*) Russians. Very dangerous men.

Georgia (*scoldingly*) And women.

Tricia Georgia! I wasn't gonna mention the women.

Anna Worse than the men?

Tricia Much. I wish Georgia had kept her mouth shut. I didn't want to frighten anyone.

Anna Well, what are these women like? How can they be so terrible?

Tricia You know Pat off *Eastenders*? They all look like her. They're not really human. They're sort of robots. They're programmed to kill. They've all got really long, sharp, red nails like Pat's. If you was to clean out their nails, you'd find dried up flesh and blood under 'em, from where they'd scraped off little children's faces.

Horrified expressions. **Anna** *tentatively touches her face.*

Tricia The men give the orders. The women are just sort of like killing machines.

Anna (*smiling unsurely*) No.

Tricia It's an experiment. An evil plot.

Jonathan *has been quietly listening, horrified.*

Jonathan They wouldn't pick us. They'd want people who were properly trained.

Tricia No that's the whole point. They've got to put down people who don't know anything about the experiment. People who aren't gonna snitch on them – school children. It's obvious. People they can 'nipulate. We've gotta be young so they've got longer to watch us before we die. (*Pause.*) It's all top secret stuff.

Anna You mean we're goin' down there for the rest of our lives?

Tricia Yeah. Why'd you think I got homesick at the beginning? D'you think I'd get homesick if I was just going to Alton Towers for the day? No, of course I wouldn't. But for the rest of my life? Well, you can see why I was upset.

Anna But I didn't even say goodbye to my mum. I just told her not to forget to record *Neighbours*.

Tricia   Ah well. It's too late now. And you're gonna miss *Neighbours* for the rest of your life.

Georgia   Doesn't matter anyway. It's ending soon.

Anna   Isn't there any way of getting out of it?

Tricia   'Fraid not.

Anna   Well, shouldn't we tell Miss Sheehan?

Tricia   She's in on it. So's the coach-driver. There's no hope I'm afraid.

Anna   Miss!

Tricia   You could ask her. But she's gonna deny it, 'cos they're not gonna tell us until there's no way out. They can't take the risk.

Anna   Miss!

Tricia   Miss Sheehan's a Russian spy. She's trying to find out about the centre of the Earth for the Russians so they can burrow underneath and set up camp there and then spring up from the sewers when we're least expecting it and kill us all and take over the world.

Anna   But Miss Sheehan always seemed so nice.

Tricia   I know. I'm sorry you had to learn this way. Shut up, James.

Jonathan   (*to* **Tricia**) How do you know all this?

Tricia   Well, it makes sense, doesn't it?

Tom   (*shyly*) I heard Mr Harris and Miss Sheehan talking.

Georgia   Mr Harris?

Tom   Yes.

Jonathan   What were they sayin'?

Tom   That the school journey . . . urm . . . might not go . . . urm . . . quite as planned, and that knowing us we'd all end up lost.

Tricia   Mmm. They were talkin' in code.

Anna   Mr Harris is one of them?

Tricia   All the teachers are. Those meetings they have. They're all to plan how they're gonna capture us. It was Mr Harris's idea. This school journey. Evil plot. He's a nasty piece of work is Harris. His wife's one of those 'Pat' robots. Flesh under her nails.

Anna   I've met her. She's nothing like that.

Tricia   Obviously not to meet people. By day she's a nice, kind old lady. By night it's all a bit more sin'ster.

Anna   I met her at 8.30 in the evenin'.

Tricia   You were lucky then. The change happens at 9.00. Half hour more and you'd have no face.

Anna   Now I think about it she did suddenly run off at about ten to nine. Some meeting or something.

Georgia   Really?

Anna   Yes.

Georgia   That's spooky.

Jonathan   But I still don't understand how come you know about all this Russian spy bit.

Tricia   Ah well. That's a bit more clever. For a start, Sheehankov is a Russian name, but to fool us all she's cunningly missed off the 'kov' bit. And also purple is the National colour of Russia, and, as we all know, purple is Miss Sheehan (or should I call her Miss Sheehankov)'s favouite colour.

They look astoundedly at Miss Sheehan(kov). The look on their faces shows that she is indeed wearing purple.

Georgia   (*tentatively*) Purple's not Russia's national colour.

Tricia   Yes it is. Ask my mum. Ask my grandad. Ask my cat. Ask my dog. Ask my goldfish . . .

Georgia   I don't like your family so I ain't gonna ask them nothin'.

Tricia   Anway, that ain't the point. Point is we're on a school journey to the centre of the Earth.

Rab   (*popping up*) Bollocks.

Anna   (*unsure*) Yeah.

Tricia   No.

Rab   You ever thought about seein' a sacriatrist?

Tricia   If that's a fizzyachrist, then no.

Rab   That's what I said. Fizzyactrist.

Tricia   Look. That's got nothin' to do with anything. We are goin' to the centre of the Earth.

Hal   (*popping up*) What's this?

Georgia   Trish reckons we're goin' to the centre of the Earth, wiv Russian spies or sommink.

Ben   (*popping up*) The cold war ended in –

Rab
Tricia
Hal   } Shut up, Mr Bean!
Georgia
Anna

Tricia   Look at the facts of the matter . . .

William   There are no facts. Only guesses.

Tricia   You shut up. How old are you?

William   (*smugly*) Ten in three weeks. How old are you?

Tricia   Yeah, well that don't matter. A few months don't make no difference to anyone. Anyway, Clever-Arse – who's to say that those guesses aren't right. No one knows.

William   Exactly. No one knows. But science suggests that it is too hot for anything to live down there.

Tricia   I don't know what scientists you've been chattin' with, Zit Face, but one that I've spoken to lives down there. How about that? So much for all your science crap. I actually know a scientist that lives down there.

She sticks her tongue out at **William**.

Rab   Gutted, Zit Face! That was cool, Trish. Pity you were talkin' outta your bum.

James   Well who else's bum would she be talkin' out of?

Rab *and* **James** *slap hands*.

Tricia   Fine. When you get down there you'll be sorry. You'll wish you listened to your dear old mate, Trish, when those monsters come for you.

Anna   Monsters?

Tricia   Yeah, the Russians reckon that's gonna be their biggest problem, the monsters.

Anna   Why, are they dangerous?

Tricia   Yeah, they're huge. They could crush you with one hand. For the Russians, they'll need two.

Rab   You've been watchin' too many moves, Trish.

James   Yeah, those 'U's that you've been watching 'ave gone straight to your head.

Rab   Yeah, like *Bambi and the Elves have a Picnic*!

Hal   I only watch '18's.

James   Have you seen *Freddy 5*?

Hal   Yeah.

James   Did you like the bit when the blood gushes out of her stomach and all the veins in her neck are ripped out?

Hal   Oh yeah. That bit. Oh yeah, that's a good bit.

James   Yeah? Well, I've got you 'cos that bit's in *Freddy 6* so you lied. Waah. Gutted.

Hal   No, I thought you said '6'.

Rab   Who's seen *The Fugitive*? (*Note: update as appropriate.*)

Louise   Yeah. It's wicked. It's the best.

James   I thought it was crap.

Louise   Yeah, I s'pose it wasn't that good.

Rab   What's your favourite bit?

Louise   Oh, urm . . . I saw it ages ago so . . . urm I can't really remember.

James   It's only just come out.

Louise   (*desperate*) Oh. Maybe I'm gettin' it muddled up with another film . . .

Rab   Which other film?

Louise   I don't know what it's called. I saw it ages ago.

James   So you haven't actually seen *The Fugitive*?

Louise   Urm . . . No. I don't think I have. I got muddled.

Rab   Do you like the bit when he jumps out of the bus?

Louise   I told you. I haven't seen it.

Rab   No, but that bit's on the trailer. You must've seen it on TV.

Louise   Oh yeah. 'Course.

Louise *turns her Gameboy on, and is abnormally engrossed in it.*

Pause.

Anna   (*to* **Sonny**) Did you know we were on a school journey to the centre of the Earth?

Rab   Some bollocks about monsters.

Tricia   That's right. Thanks Rab.

Sonny   Did Tricia tell you this?

Anna   Yeah.

Sonny   Don't believe anything she says. She has these funny turns, see. I just let her get on with it.

Tricia *doesn't seem too bothered about this interruption.*

Tricia   You'll be sorry.

The coach goes through a tunnel, plunging the children into momentary darkness. When the coach re-emerges there is a slight pause.

The coach stops at traffic lights.

Richard   Tax that Ford Cortina – no shares!

Jonathan   I've already taxed it.

Richard   No, you can't. I said 'no shares'.

Jonathan   No, I got it ages ago.

Rab   Tax that BMW! – No shares!

Richard
Jonathan } Tax that Mercedes Benz!
Rab

Richard   I got that.

Jonathan   I don't fink so.

Richard   I did.

Chrissy   Tax that lamb.

Rab   (*spastic noises*) You can't tax lambs. You can only tax cars.

Chrissy   Why shouldn't you be able to tax lambs?

Rab   'Cos it's the rule. You 'tax' cars and 'bags' sheeps.

Chrissy   Bags that lamb! – No shares.

The boys exchange looks.

James   Whoever nicked my Twix had best gissit back unless they wanna die a painful and slow death.

Hal   Moose! Stress! Watch it, everyone. James might turn nasty.

Jonathan   How do you get down to the centre of the Earth? I mean, how would you, supposin' we was goin' which I don't believe anyway.

Tricia   Ah, well. That's the cunning bit. You know the roller-coaster at Alton Towers?

Louise   Yeah. The Corkscrew.

Rab   Yeah, it's wicked, man.

Hal   Yeah, that bit when it dips down is blindin'.

Tricia   Yeah, well anyway. Miss Sheehankov will give . . .

Louise   Sheehankov?

Jonathan   It's Miss Sheehan's secret Russian name.

Louise   Oh, right.

Tricia   Yeah, well she'll give the signal when the train's filled up with us lot, and the man what works the Corkscrew will switch the tracks so instead of goin' back to the beginning, the ground opens up and we go plummeting down into the centre of the Earth.

James   Wicked.

Louise   Yeah, like a kind of roller-coaster in the dark.

James   Mad.

Anna   But won't other people see us go down inside the Earth?

Tricia   No. 'Cos this like – see – urm – this invisibility shield thing gets activated as we get to a certain point on the ride and we go down and no one sees. It's well advanced.

Tom   Wow. Those Russians are clever.

Hal   Yeah.

Anna   But our parents will notice we've gone.

Tricia   For a while, yeah. But you know all these kids that vanish like when they're skiin' and stuff?

Louise   Yeah?

Tricia   That's where they've gone. We'll probably see them down there.

Rab   They died, didn't they?

Tricia   That's what everyone was told. But it's all part of a 'spirisy.

Anna   'Spirisy?

Tricia   That's what it is. A 'spirisy.

James   But how did these skiing dead kids get down?

Tricia   Similar way. Only the chair-lift things suddenly change course and go down.

Louise   So what they gonna say happened to us?

Tricia   Oh, we'll probably be one of those 'School Bus Off Cliff' tragedies.

Rab   You talk the biggest pile of crud ever.

Tricia   No, but no, shut up, right, no shut up, listen right. I know it sounds stupid but I mean, it sounded stupid to me when I first heard it from the head of The British Intelligence . . .

Tom   You said you put two and two together.

Tricia   Ah, well, my dear Tom. I'm afraid it's a bit more complicated than that. I am in fact a spy. Working under cover. Posing as just an ordinary schoolgirl, when actually I am Britain's last hope at exposing this 'spirisy. I shouldn't be telling you this. I could be putting you all in mortal danger.

Pause.

Rab   No. (*Pause.*) Carry on.

Tricia   No. I musn't. If the Russians found out that you knew they'd probably murder you. Pull your heads off with this special new machine that – like – pulls your head off. It like sort of twists it a bit to get it loose – yeah – and then it pulls it off really slowly – like – stretches it off.

Hal   What's wrong with the electric chair?

Tricia   No. That's too fast. They want it slow.

James   I'm gonna be a Torture and Killing Machine designer when I'm older. I'm gonna design things like what you've never heard of. That like has little stabbing little pins and sucks the jelly bit in your eyes out so they shrivel up and fall out and like cuts this hole in your tummy and cuts into your guts and pulls your hairs out one by one, and, for like, old men, it would do your nostril hairs as well . . .

Tom   Yeah, but . . .

James   No. Quiet. I'm talking. It pulls your fingers out and sticks sharp points up your nostrils that makes it bleed everywhere and it pierces your brain, and it's red hot – no, white hot, so it frazzles your brain but you don't die yet because your brain's not completely burned yet, and you can still feel pain. And sharp knives dig under your finger-nails . . .

Rab   Before or after they've been pulled out?

James   Shut up! (*Eyes widen – a terrifying glare.*) Before. And then, when your brain's burned out completely, and your eyes have fallen out, and your fingers have been pulled out, then this thing will come out and it will chicken-scratch your heart until you're dead. (*Rubs his hands and grins.*)

Silence – shocked faces.

Rab   (*sarcastically*) Nice job.

James   Or I might be a doctor.

Pause.

Ben   You could be both. (*Pause.*) Being a doctor would give you access to people to test your equipment on.

James   (*seeing it. Dreamily*) A wicked doctor . . . !

Tricia   Has this got anything to do with what I was sayin'?

James   You was talkin' about the Russian Killing Machine.

Tricia   Yeah, but that doesn't mean you can just go ravin' on like sommink out of *Freddy 5*. So shut it.

James   Yeah, well someone nicked my Twix. I was annoyed, innit?

Tricia   You're such a weirdo.

Ben   Don't, Tricia. His sadistic tendencies may be useful to us when we get there.

Tricia   Yeah, whatever.

Rab   Urgggh, Tom, don't come near me with those shoes! They went . . .

James   Oh gosh!

Rab   No, listen, they went out when the dinosaurs came in!

James   That's sad.

Rab   Yeah, I know. – But I just said it to keep in with Tom.

James   That's wicked. Oh gosh. You – got – told!

Hal   You gonna take that, man? Nah don't take it.

Rab   Arrgh. You gonna beat me up, Tom? No, Tom, please don't beat me up. I'll have to go and find Mumsy.

James   Where does your mum shop, Tom? Oxfam?

Rab   No, Ultra Oxfam!

Tricia   Listen!

Rab   Tom. Did you know?

James   Did you know? Did you know?

Rab   That cats lay eggs. That's true actually, please.

Tom   No they don't.

Rab   Yes they do cos my dad told me actually.

James   An' his dad's a scientist.

Rab   Did you know that?

Tom   Yeah.

Hysterical laughing.

Tom   (*desperate*) They don't lay eggs. I was joking. They don't lay eggs. I was just testin' you out.

Rab   Gutted. Vexed. How – do – you – feel?

James   'At was wicked. 'At was wicked.

Tom   (*desperately*) They don't lay eggs. I know they don't.

Rab   Aw, what a nice 'Snoopy' lunch box, Tom. Was it part of the Oxfam summer sale? Ultra mega Oxfamopolis.

Tricia   (*to* **James**) I don't think Louise's got a TV.

James   What!

Tricia   All that rubbish about *The Fugitive*. I reckon she hasn't got one.

Georgia   (*leaning in to the conversation*) When I went to her house she said it was at the mender's.

Tricia   How long ago was this?

Georgia   About three months ago.

James   She ain't got a TV? Oi, Rab. Get this. Louise ain't got a telly!

Rab   Waaah! Shamed. Louise! (*In front of the whole coach.*) Ain't you got a telly?

Louise   What?

James   You haven't got a telly!

Louise   Of course I do.

James   Oo yeah.

Louise   I do.

Rab   Alright then. How does the 'Wash and Go' advert go then?

Louise   Isn't that the one when . . . there's a lake or something and . . .

Rab ⎫ Take two bottles into the shower? Not me. I just want to wash my hair
James ⎭ and go. And now I can with new Vidal Sassoon 'Wash and Go.'

(*They flip their heads as done by ladies in shampoo adverts to show how silky-soft their hair is. Note: Update as appropriate.*)

Tricia   Why didn't you tell us, Lou? You shoulda know we'd understand.

James   (*chanting*) Louise ain't got a telly! Louise ain't got a telly!

Rab   Why don't yer tell yer mum to get one from Oxfam? Ultra-mega-all-yer-needs-Oxfam-opapopolis.

Hysterical laughing.

Hal   (*pause*) You ever been to a funeral?

James   Yeah.

Hal   Yeah, what happens, then?

James   They bury people, don't they?

Hal   Yeah, but . . .

James   Yeah. I should know. I go to funerals every single Monday.

Sonny   No, you don't.

James   An' I go to bonfires as well. That's when they put someone in the bonfire and watch them die slowly. – And then laugh. And then they get all the ashes and make the relatives eat it.

Hal   Doesn't it taste 'orrible though?

James   It tastes of them. Like, if I were to bite a bit out of you now, right, and taste it. If someone burnt . . .

Sonny   And you . . .

James   No, listen, right. If I were to bite you now, I'd taste you and remember that taste, right, and then if someone burnt loads of people and put all their ashes in bowls; I could taste each one and see which one was you.

Hal   Really?

James   Yeah.

Hal   Shall we try it?

James   Ain't touchin' you.

Hal   I don't mean me.

Pause.

James   Sonny?

Sonny   Yeah?

James Would you mind if we – urm – if we took a bite out of your leg and then burnt you with loads of other people and then tried you with a small spoon?

Sonny (*after a moment's thought*) Alright.

James You go first.

Hal It was your idea.

James No, I've done it so often.

Hal Well, I don't want to lose my appetite. And anyway. They don't burn people.

James They do. It's called cremations. Sometimes they give yer the ashes to take home in pots, other times people leave it there, and it gets given to cannibal countries. They prefer it to 'Nescafé'.

Sonny Cup-a-soup for cannibals. (*Pause.*) My dad's friend who's a farmer . . .

Hal Your dad's friend's not a farmer.

Sonny He is.

Hal You dad hasn't got any friends.

Sonny He has.

Hal You haven't got a dad.

Sonny I have! Like I was sayin' right, my dad's friend who's a farmer . . .

Hal Get on with it.

Sonny He got caught under a tractor.

James *makes an annoying and loud noise with the ashtray on the seat in front.*

Hal What?

Sonny He got caught under a tractor . . .

James (*without sympathy*) Did he die? Did he?

Sonny No. He was alright.

James Yeah? Which bit of him got mashed?

Sonny His legs. He ain't got no legs no more.

James What happened to his legs?

Sonny They got caught under the tractor, didn't they?

James Yeah, but where are they now?

Sonny They probably buried them.

Hal Yeah, you go to funerals. Ain't you ever seen legs buried?

James No, they only bury whole bodies where I go. But I've just had an idea.

Sonny What?

James Wouldn't it be cheaper to bury all your bits, like, separate, than buryin' them altogether. And also you'd get to have loads of funerals, like, one for your leg and one for your head. And you could go to your own funeral. Not your head's funeral obviously – or your heart's. But you could probably see off a leg or two before you died of blood loss. And . . .

Hal It wouldn't be cheaper because you'd have to buy loads of different sized coffins. And they'd all have to be made specially to order, 'cos they don't normally make 'em different sizes to just ordinary people.

James Yeah. Some rich people get coffins for their cats and dogs. I'd need two dog ones, one for each leg; and two cat ones for my arms. And a small sheep one for my middle bit.

Hal It still wouldn't be cheaper. What might be quite cheap though, now I've thought about it, would be if you chopped yourself up . . .

Sonny How are you s'posed to chop yourself up if you're dead?

Hal Alright, get someone else to do it, and then fit yourself into your coffin, so you can fit into a smaller coffin. That would be cheaper.

James Yeah, but it wouldn't be very nice for people who have to look at you in your coffin at your funeral. 'Cos that's what you have to do.

Hal What?

James You have to all stand around lookin' at the dead person. It's tradition. But shall I tell you what happened one time? I was lookin' at this dead person in their coffin one Monday, yeah. An' I was chewin' a bit of chewin' gum, right. And it dropped out of my mouth right into the dead person's mouth. This guy that worked there or sommink got it and gave it back to me. But I told him to keep it 'cos I didn't want it any more.

Matthew You know that thing 'bout buryin' bits separate? It'd be a good idea to find out who really cared about you. (*Pause – people begin to lose interest.*) It'd be a good idea for my mum 'cos she's always pretendin' to suicide herself to see if we care . . .

Hal And do you?

Matthew We pretend to. (*With pride.*) If you've got a mad mum like me, you have to have a man from the council round every week to check on you.

Hal (*impressed*) Wow.

There is a pause. Everyone is semi-still. Then **Emma**'s *face slowly rises up from behind the seats.*

Anna (*quietly*) What's it like down there, Tricia?

Tricia Down where? On the floor of the coach? I dunno. It's sort of . . .

Anna No, the centre of the Earth.

Tricia Oh that. Oh I dunno. There's caves an' stuff. (*It is obvious that* **Tricia** *has tired of the subject.*)

Anna Will there be any lights? I can't go to sleep without a light on.

Tricia (*realizing she's really 'caught' one*) Well, yeah. Of course the Russians are gonna make sure that there's some light otherwise they won't be able to see us through the video cameras to watch how we live.

Anna So there will be some light?

Tricia Yeah. There will be light. But wouldn't you rather live a life of darkness than know that you're being watched day after day, night after night?

Anna Er . . . well, no. You see I can't go to sleep without a light.

Tricia Oh yeah. You said.

Tricia *tries to join the others' conversation – which is far more lively – but* **Anna** *tugs at her arm.*

Anna Will we have someone on guard all night for those monsters?

Tricia Er . . . Yeah.

Anna Do I have to do it, Tricia? I don't think girls should have to do it.

Tricia No, sorry. Everyone has to do it.

Rab (*whose face has been wedged between the two seats throughout the entire conversation*) Waaaah! Gutted! I can't believe that you think all this crud is actually true!

Anna It could be true. It could be true. We don't know. Nobody knows. Why shouldn't there be a world of caves and passages down there? (*Everyone is now listening.*) I bet the monsters who live down there say exactly the same thing. They say 'how could there be a world up there? It's impossible.' But it's not. 'Cos we live here and we know that it's perfectly possible. And I bet the only reason that those monsters haven't yet invaded us is because of monsters like you sayin': 'Nah, it's all a pile of crud.'

Rab Well, thank God for monsters like me.

Louise You're bad enough as a 'uman. I don't fink I could handle it if there was a monster like you as well.

Tom   But Anna's got a point. – Not saying that there are monsters or nothin' – but, I mean, we can't know can we? – I mean – for sure.

Anna   Yeah. And Tricia heard it from the head of The British Intelligence. If you can't trust the head of The British Intelligence then who can you trust?

Louise   That's true.

Ben   I think it is true.

Rab   He speaks . . .

Louise   Shut up, Rab. Let him have his say.

Rab   Shup. You ain't gotta telly.

Louise   What d'you think's true, Mr Bean?

Ben   I think it is very possible that people could actually journey to the centre of the Earth. (*Pause.*) Tricia's accounts have in fact been (*Pause.*) most accurate.

Rab   Tricia's whats have been what?

Tricia   How would you know? I mean, they have been, but how the heck do you know that?

Ben   (*pause*) I've been there.

Tricia   Shut up.

Anna   How did you get down?

Ben   In a chair-lift. (*Pause.*) Like Tricia said.

Tricia   You can't of done.

Anna   Is there any light?

Tricia   I've already told you that there is.

Anna   Well, yes but, I mean, Ben's actually been there, so he's more likely to know for sure, isn't he?

Ben   Don't worry, Anna. (*Pause.*) There is some light. Things produce their own natural light. (*Pause.*) Like glow worms.

Anna   Oh, good.

Tricia   He doesn't know what he's talkin' about.

Anna   He's been there. You've only heard about it from The British Intelligence.

Ben   Oh? What is it like then?

Tricia   Well, the area I went to, know as . . . urm . . . Lower Beemsbry, was made up of these huge caves. Dark, 'cept for when the light from the glow worms shone on the bits of jewels in the walls. Lower Beemsbry is like the capital – 'cos it's the most beautiful area. There were dark passages everywhere, like corridors, leading off into different rooms. The floor's soft and sandy – it's actually jewel dust – so it sparkles. When I came back I still had some jewel dust on my shoes . . .

Rab   Let's see.

Tricia   It's rubbed off now, stupid. Anyway, there are glow worms, like Ben said. And glow maggots. And the Russians have glow eels. I slept in one of the small caves – I had a huge, flat rock as a bedside table. I was only there for two days.

Everyone looks at **Ben** *for a confirmation.*

Anna   Ben?

Ben   It's nothing like that. And there's no glow eels.

Rab   Gutted. Nice imagination, Trish.

William   It's too hot down there.

Ben   Not if you wear this stuff called 'Starlite' that a hairdresser in Manchester invented. (*Pause.*) A suit of 'Starlite', you could sit on the sun and be OK – on the surface only, obviously. No one believed this hairdresser, (*Pause.*) the 'Starlite' was mouldable like plastic and yet virtually completely heat proof. (*Pause.*) Impossible, scientists said. But they tested it, and the lazer they used to test it with – which burns through slabs of iron in a millisecond – broke due to the reflection of heat. (*Pause.*) It was on television, but it was on channel four so none of you'll have watched it. Hairdresser. In Manchester.

Pause.

Anna   (*who appears to have been thinking hard*) Miss! Miss! Is Alton Towers near Manchester?

Miss Sheehan speaks.

The children look at each other for a tense moment.

Hal   Wow.

Tricia   Mr Bean's lying.

Anna   Ben is not lying.

When **Ben** *pauses, he looks at his audience through his extra-strong lens glasses and sucks medatively on his pencil.*

Tricia   He is. I'm the spy. I know what's going on. Ben's just makin' it up. He's never been there.

Ben   Unlike you. (*Pause.*) I'm not one to boast about my part in such a serious affair as this.

Tricia   Just 'cos you can say lots of stupid words that don't mean anything to anyone, you think you're really cool.

Anna   What do we sleep on?

Ben   Erm . . . Oh, well when I was there we slept on . . . erm . . . rocks . . .

Louise   How uncomfortable. Was it really bad?

Tricia   Don't be ridiculous. If the Russians' experiment is to find out if they can live there, they're gonna give us the same things that they'd have. And I bet you *they* won't be sleeping on rocks.

Ben   That's what I was about to say. (*Pause.*) I went before the Russians had set up this experiment. (*Pause.*) I was the first ever person there.

Tricia   The experiment was set up in 1936. November. That's before you were born.

Ben   Ah, yes. But the West side of the centre of the Earth. Not the bit that everyone goes to. (*Pause.*) If you know so much about all this, tell me the name of the Russian spy who is in charge.

Tricia   Radkot Flipscoddle.

Ben   That doesn't sound Russian.

Tricia   Obviously. It's a codename. (*Pause.*) Alright then, what's his real name?

Ben *hesitates for a moment.*

Tricia   You don't know.

Ben   No, I'm just wondering whether it's wise to tell you. (*Pause.*) How do I know you are really who you say you are?

Tricia   Oh this is stupid. I know you're lying. You know you're lying. So why bother?

Louise   You just wanna have all the attention, Tricia. You just wanna be the one who knows it all. And you can't stand it when someone knows more than you, can you?

Tricia   (*shouting*) It's got nothing to do with that! I know he's lying.

Louise   So he's lying and you're not? Is that it. Everything you say goes. Everything he says is crud? Is that it?

Tricia   No, that's not it.

Louise   Well, that's certainly what it seems like, Tricia.

Tricia   Piss off, Louise. This has got nothin' to do with you.

Anna   This has got everything to do with Louise and everyone else in class J5. It's all of us that have gotta face this.

Tricia   (*shouting*) Will you all just shut up and listen to me? I know that Ben is lying because . . . because I made the whole thing up.

Rab   Yeah, that's what we said.

Tricia   No. Everything. The whole lot. None of it's true.

Long silence.

Anna   Tricia, we all know you're tryin' to protect us from findin' out too much for our own safety – and it's very good of you – but now I think it's time that we all faced facts. Don't you?

Long pause.

Tricia   Yes. It's time. You're right. And it was for your protection. I should of known I couldn't fool yous lot.

Anna   So, Mr Bean. Are you a spy?

Ben   Well, as a matter of fact (*Pause.*) yes, I am.

As everyone crowds around **Ben. Tricia** *sulks in the background. Her arms are folded, and whenever* **Ben** *says something she shakes her head scornfully.*

Jonathan   Surely you shouldn't say that in case one of us is a Russian spy.

Ben   Yes, (*Pause.*) and I have my suspicions. (*He nods towards the unaware* **Tricia***.*)

Louise   (*whispering*) Tricia? No.

Ben   (*leaning in to his eager listeners*) The name she gave of the Russian spy leader?

Anna   Yes?

Ben   She said it was the codename?

Anna   Yes.

Ben   The British don't know that codename. It's something we've been trying to discover for years.

Louise   Then how come she knows it?

Ben   I wonder.

Anna   If it is true, then she'll try and warn Sheehankov. Try an' tell her that we know.

Louise . Georgia, it's alright. How long 'till we're there?

Ben   (*looks at his watch*) Ten minutes.

Anna   Ten?

Rab *and* **James** *can be heard screeching with laughter from behind the seats.*

James   Look! Look! (*Producing one of the see-through sick-bags which appears to be full of vomit.*)

Rab   (*leaning over and pretending to be violently sick into the bag*) I've been sick! (*He passes the bag around for closer inspection.*)

Hal   I'm gonna make one too. (*She rummages around in her packed lunch, looking for things with which to concoct another bag of sick.*)

Georgia   I'm actually gonna be sick.

Hal *and* **Rab** *waft the fake sick in* **Georgia**'s *face, while making sick noises.*

Miss Sheehan speaks.

Hal }
Rab }   Nothin' Miss.

Miss Sheehan speaks.

The reaction her last statement has provoked is one of utter disgust.

Tricia   That's disgustin' Miss. You can't make us do that.

Miss Sheehan speaks.

Tricia   Yeah. But it's all mashed up.

Georgia   I'm not jokin'. I'm gonna be sick. Get me a sick bag – quick!

Jonathan   They're all filled with mashed up pack lunch!

Georgia   Just get me anything! Quick!

Anna   Here's one. (*Handing* **Georgia** *one of the see-through sick-bags.*)

Georgia *attempts to open the bag, but it's one of those plastic ones that stick together and you can't tell which end is which.*

Georgia   (*desperate*) I can't get it open!

Eventually **Georgia** *manages to open it, and is sick – much to everyone's enjoyment.*

James   Look! Look! She 'ad egg for breakfast. She was the one who guffed!

Rab   Excuse me, Miss. But Georgia's just done exactly what you told us not to. She's put all her pack lunch – all mashed up – into a sick bag!

Chrissy   Miss said the next one would have to eat it.

Rab   (*triumphantly*) I know.

James   'At's wicked. Rab, gimme skin. You're a funny guy.

Louise   Sheehan!

Miss Sheehan speaks.

Georgia   No it's really sick, Miss.

Chrissy   Rab was tryin' to get her into trouble.

Miss Sheehan speaks.

Rab   No Miss! (*Everyone has burst out laughing and is pushing the bag of sick towards* **Rab**.) No! Please Miss. That's not funny. It's not even my sick! – I don't like egg! Please Miss. I was jokin'. Please Miss don't make me Miss! (*He is almost in tears.*) I'm sorry.

Miss Sheehan speaks.

Everyone reluctantly withdraws from **Rab**.

Rab   Thanks, Miss Sheehankov – urm Sheehan. Sorry, I meant Sheehan.

Everyone is glaring at **Rab** *when he turns back to face them.*

I slipped.

Tom   You slipped? You slipped? You idiot! You fool. Now Miss Sheehankov knows that we know. There's no chance of escape now!

Louise   Look! Look! She's talkin' to the coach-driver. She's telling him that we know.

Tom   There's no hope. You idiot!

Anna   We should make plans.

Rab   I'm really sorry.

Anna OK. Apology accepted. Now, come on. Let's decide what we're gonna do.

Georgia *suddenly bursts into tears.*

Georgia I'm scared.

Rab Don't worry, George. It's all gonna be fine.

Anna Georgia. Keep it down. If Sheehankov hears you she'll be over here like a shot.

Louise (*hissing*) She's coming!

Everyone sits back in their seats suddenly.

James (*smiling sweetly*) Hello, Miss.

Anna *budges up reluctantly to make room for Miss Sheehan(kov).*

Anna (*replying to a question from Miss*) Yes. The dodgems are fun.

Miss Sheehan speaks.

Anna (*catching eyes with* **Ben**; *quietly*) Yeah . . . I probably will be going on the roller-coaster . . . Miss.

Miss Sheehan speaks.

Anna Yeah, alright. See you later, Miss.

All look at each other as Miss Sheehan returns to her seat.

Louise She knows.

Rab (*to* **Anna**) What's the plan?

Anna We are going to have to get control of the coach. Ben?

Ben *nods solemnly.*

James Five minutes, 52 seconds.

Anna Is every one in agreement?

Solemn nods.

Tricia Don't be stupid. We can't do that. We're only kids. Can anyone drive? I mean, it's stupid. It's impossible. We are just gonna stay calm and see how it goes.

Ben *looks at* **Anna** *as if to say 'see?'*

Anna Tricia. I'm beginning to wonder whose side you're on. First you tell us you're a British spy with nerves of iron . . .

Tricia I didn't say nothin' about any iron . . .

Anna   And now it seems that you're a Russian spy, helping the Russians to capture us.

Georgia   (*suddenly lashing out at* **Tricia**, *hysterical*) You filthy Russian spy! You traitor! I can't believe I invited you to my birthday party! There's gonna be no Russian spies at my birthday party! You traitor! You cow! I hate you!

Georgia *breaks down in sobs.*

Tricia   Georgia! I'm not a Russian spy. I'm not any sort of spy!

Ben   As I suspected.

Tricia   (*almost screaming*) Shut up! You're the evil one! You deserve to die!

Anna *grabs hold of* **Tricia** *by the shoulders.*

Anna   Shut up! You're hysterical! Shut up. Sheehankov will be here any moment.

Miss Sheehan speaks.

Anna }
Ben }   Nothin' Miss.

Anna   Now, everyone just stay calm. Georgia do you need another sick bag?

Georgia *nods.*

Find her a sick bag please, Hal.

Hal   OK.

Anna   Now, we need to decide who's in charge of what.

James   Rab an' me'll be in charge of the battle tactics.

Rab   Now, has everyone got weapons?

Tom   Oh yeah. I'll just get my Kalashnikov out of my backpack. You fool. 'Course we haven't got weapons.

Louise   What d'we need 'em for anyway?

Rab   If we're tryin' to take over the coach, I don't think it's gonna be too effective if we go up there and say: 'Now, we know you're workin' for the Russians, and that you are involved in an evil plot to send us to the centre of the Earth. So if you'd both jump out of the window we'd be most grateful. – Oh, but before you jump you couldn't teach us how to drive this thing, could you?' They'd just call for reinforcements and then we'd be done for. No. This thing has gotta be done usin' surprise tactics and weapons.

Hal   Well, none of us have got any knives or nothin' so what d'you suggest?

James   Pack lunch boxes? I mean, anything that will hurt if it hits you.

Hal   Oranges. My mum packed five. Vitamin C.

Hal *passes the oranges around.*

Anna   OK James, Rab. How do you suggest we take over the coach?

James   Rab an' me'll crawl to the front of the coach an' get ready behind the driver. Then yous lot, after countin' to ten . . .

Tom   Silently.

James   Yeah, obviously. Anyway . . .

William   If we all suddenly go silent they'll know something's going on.

Hal   Go on, James.

Anna   No, William's right. It needs to be better planned.

Louise   How long have we got?

James   Two minutes, 21 seconds.

Anna   William, what do you think?

William   I think it would be better if we sing a song and then arrange a certain point . . .

James   Yeah, whatever. Anyway, when you get to this certain point, you all charge to the front and attack Sheehankov . . .

Tricia   NO!

Anna   Is there a problem with this plan?

Tricia   Yes. What if Miss Sheehankov – I mean Miss Sheehan – isn't a Russian spy after all?

Hal   If she's not a Russian spy then why's she taking us to the centre of the Earth?

Tricia   Maybe she's not.

James   42 seconds. What are you gonna sing?

Hal   (*to* **Tricia**) Why d'you think that?

Tricia   I made it all up.

Hal *looks at the crowd of excited children and then back to* **Tricia**.

Hal   Why?

Louise   What about 'Glory Glory 'Allelujah'?

Tricia   (*to* **Hal**) Just a bit of fun.

Tom   Three times through.

James   (*looking at watch; loudly whispering*) 12, 11, 10 . . .

The others excitedly join in.

9, 8, 7 . . .

Emma   (*suddenly standing*) I've had an idea!

A pause. The children look questioningly at **Emma**.

James   5, 4, 3, 2, 1

Anna   Glory Glory Hallelujah,
Teacher hit me with the ruler.
Ruler snapped in half,
An' we all began to laugh,
An' she ain't gonna teach no more –
Break the door!

Tricia *grabs* **Hal***'s arm as* **Hal** *begins to sing.*

Tricia   I think they've gone mad.

Everyone begins to sing as **Rab** *and* **James** *crawl to the front of the bus. They hide behind the driver (invisible), each armed with a pack lunch box and an orange.*

As the children get towards the end of the third time through they begin to sing in loud, excited voices.

Tricia, Ben *and* **Emma** *remain seated.* **Tricia** *and* **Ben** *catch eyes and stare at each other.* **Tricia** *shakes her head at him in disgust.*

Suddenly they charge towards the audience, shrieking. **Hal** *glances back at* **Tricia***. She pauses for a moment them continues running.*

They attack the invisible teacher and driver.

James   *(while attacking the driver)* Take that, you evil Russian spy! Think you could fool us did you?

Emma *can be seen doing up her seat belt in the background.*

Suddenly it seems that the children are back on their imaginary roller-coaster, swerving and lurching. All face the audience, their faces full of fear and excitement.

Rab   Waaaaah!

Hal   Wooooh!

James   Wickeeeed!

Anna   Excellaaaant!

The Ezra Pound to Daisy's T.S.Eliot

Daisy Campbell and Ken Campbell interviewed by Jim Mulligan

Ken Campbell has been writing for as long as Daisy Campbell can remember. Her earliest memories are of seeing him at the typewriter, hearing the sound of the keys and writing her own stories at the age of two, covering the page with random letters and 'reading' the story to her parents. At the age of four she broke the 'Q' key, so that for years Ken Campbell had to write plays that didn't have a 'Q' in them. When the Royal National Theatre asked Ken Campbell to write a play that children could perform he agreed.

'I used to write plays for children but then I had a connection with my own childhood. In a sense I was saying: this is the kind of play we should have had when I was a child. But I don't really know anything about children now so I suggested I should collaborate with Daisy. She was a novelist from the age of seven-and-a-half to nine and I suggested we should adapt one of her stories. She agreed but when she saw how much money was involved she wanted to do the lot. We did of course collaborate, but my role was mainly suggesting what should be cut out and putting in three jokes. If you like, I was Ezra Pound to her T.S. Eliot.'

Daisy's version of events is substantially the same. 'At my primary school we were given a lot of freedom to do the things we wanted and I wrote *School Journey to the Centre of the Earth* over months. It was about my class and they loved it. They couldn't wait for the instalments to be written so that I could perform the story for them every week. I chose different character traits and exaggerated them. Later on, I tried to adapt it into a film script and then a radio play. Then, when my Dad was asked to write the play for the National, he offered to buy the title from me. Then he said, actually, you could do the whole thing. To begin with, we were going to stick to the idea of the children going to the centre of the earth but we realised that children talking are so clever and funny and imaginative that they need never get off the coach.'

School Journey to the Centre of the Earth is, on the surface, a lighthearted play. Daisy Campbell has captured the voices of children and it is possible that adults will recollect the time when they were children with imaginations that allowed them to believe in anything. In Tricia, she has created a 'Just William' character. 'William could put ideas in all the Outlaws' heads so easily and so convincingly that they believed there was treasure in the back garden and would go digging there. In the same way, Tricia can make the children believe their teacher is a Russian spy. Tricia craves attention. She cannot handle it when Ben takes over and uses his intelligence and knowledge of science to carry on the fantasy. Tricia is a little bit like me. I used to go around the playground saying I was the Yingo-Yong. I had five layers of skin and every time anyone touched me I would lose a layer until I became a skeleton. The others really believed it. Like Tricia, I used to test the limits to see how far I could take them. But back in the classroom, as soon as the register was called we were back to a different reality.'

There is an ineluctable logic once a child's imagination has accepted something as reality. Certain consequences follow. 'If she isn't a Russian spy, then why is she taking us to the centre of the earth?' and 'If you can't believe the Head of British Intelligence then who can you trust?' Once children have that kind of certainty, then the attack on the driver and the coach crash are inevitable. Children are anarchists. They have collective power which they hardly ever use, but once this power is unleashed, dreadful things may happen.

James is a character who might be seen as dangerous. He relishes talking about gory events. He is the expert on horror movies. He is going to be a torture-and killing-machine designer when he grows up, or he might be a doctor. He says that he goes to funerals every Monday and he speculates at length on how bodies might be cut up and buried in bits. 'I have a soft spot for James. I see him as living in a council flat with his mother. At home he is very tame which is why he lets go a bit in school. I wrote James's obsession with blood and gore into my play because it amused me. I was not passing any moral judgements one way or another. Perhaps the fact that he is so open about it all means he has a perfectly healthy attitude to violence.'

Anyone who has listened to children talking will know that their language is a riot of vulgarity, hilarity, jokes, swear words and insults. In *School Journey to the Centre of the Earth*, Daisy Campbell has very little swearing but there is an abundance of belittling comment, personal abuse and scatological ribaldry such as the woman on the toilet who is so fat her flab bulges over the side. 'Of course children use this kind of language but they know exactly when to switch it off and on. I recently went back to my primary school and as I stood near the fence the children were shouting and calling names and I was appalled. Then I went in to see some of my old teachers and saw the same kids, and butter wouldn't melt in their mouths. I thought: that's exactly what we were like when we were here.'

Ken Campbell declines to comment on children today except to say that he tries to keep away from them. With regard to this play he says: 'I don't think plays are all that difficult to write. People have made it seem as if you have to have a degree from Cambridge before you can write a play. Well you probably need to have been to Cambridge to get a play put on, but that is a different matter. I just thought that if Daisy is on her uppers it might be quite handy to know she can write a play. And that is precisely what she has done.'

Ken Campbell is a performer and writer. He played opposite Alf Garnett in *In Sickness and in Health*. He founded the Science Fiction Theatre of Liverpool, for which he directed two epic productions, *The Warp* and *Illuminatus!* which was the opening production in the Cottesloe Theatre at the National. He also founded the legendary *Ken Campbell's Roadshow*. His children's plays include *Old King Cole*, *Skungpoomery*, *Frank'n'Stein* and *Clown Plays* (with FK Waetcher). He has recently performed his trilogy of one-man shows, consisting of *Furtive*

Nudist, Pigspurt and *Jamais Vu* (the last premièred at the Cottesloe Theatre in 1993). His plays are published by Methuen Drama.

Daisy Campbell, who is sixteen, is Ken's daughter. The play has developed from an earlier work she wrote when she was nine.

School Journey to the Centre of the Earth

Production Notes

Setting and staging
The staging requires only minimal sets, depending largely on the characters working together as a chorus, on stage throughout. The Teacher and the Driver are invisible.

The play has been developed from a story Daisy Campbell based on her London classmates, but the setting can be anywhere, and so adjustment for an alternative vernacular is permissible.

The **sound** of the coach will need to be indicated, also electronic games that accompany young children on long journeys. Special effects need to include the coach crash and Georgina being sick. Passage of time and the environment outside the coach might be suggested, preferably very simply.

Casting
The cast of seventeen is aged between $8\frac{3}{4}$ (Stacy) and ten-in-three-weeks'-time (William). They can be played successfully by a young cast or an older age range, but the director should make sure the cast is fully aware of the realities of life as seen through nine-year-old eyes.

Questions
1. How does the language used by the children amongst themselves alter when they address their teacher?

2. How does Tricia draw the other children into the world of her imagination?

3. At what point does the mood of the play change and become darker? Why does this happen, and how could it be expressed in terms of the theatre?

4. Which characters appear more menacing? How can this be emphasised in production?

5. What makes other characters more vulnerable? Again, how can this be indicated on stage?

6. Which characters change in the course of the play? How might these changes be indicated by the actors playing the characters involved?

Exercises
1. In pairs, Person A has two minutes to discover as much as possible about what Person B did the previous night, and vice versa. Each person then tells the rest of the group about the other's experiences, through the eyes of a nine-year-old.

2. In groups of five, move as one body in a clump (not a line), taking the lead from the person at the front of the ensemble. Produce a verbal and physical rhythm appropriate for a group of nine-year-olds. Change your leader, and continue the rhythm. Without discussion, imagine the group are on a different journey, moving to the centre of the earth. Each time the 'leader' changes, so does the environment, which throws up a new set of challenges. The teacher or director has to shout out the new environment, e.g. 'crocodile swamp!', 'rope bridge over 1000-foot ravine!', etc.

3. In groups of four, imagine and create, through improvisation, a conversation between Tricia, Ben, Anna and Rab, who have survived childhood and are now adults.

4. As a group, pick up a chair and, at a pre-arranged signal, form a conventional coach seating pattern. Experiment with a series of states, e.g. coach departing, coach journey with computer games, night-time, sing-along, coach going round corners at speed, coach crash, etc.

5. As a group, imagine Miss Sheehan is passing down the coach. Make lots of noise, then one by one fall silent as she passes, then start up the noise again. Decide whether she is very tall, small, frail, etc.

6. In pairs, create the characters of the Driver and Miss Sheehan. Improvise the conversation they might be having moments before the coach crashes.

7. In the group, imagine a film camera is filming the journey from various angles. One by one, various members of the group become the 'news presenter'. Experiment with turning round, standing up, during which time the noise decreases while one (or more) speak, and then returns to its original volume.

8. As a group of five:
    i   Establish a convention for the coach in transit: i.e. how does the audience know that the actors are travelling?
    ii Respond to an event on the coach.
    iii Respond to an event outside the coach.
    iv Turn the coach into something else, e.g. a fridge, a roller-coaster.

Suzy Graham-Adriani,
Director/Producer for BT National Connections

Faith, Hope and Charity

a little dance of death in five acts

Ödön von Horváth

Translated by Christopher Hampton

This play was written with the help of Lukas Kristl.

Author's Aside

Passing through Munich in February 1932, I came across an acquaintance called Lukas Kristl, who for some years had been a court reporter. He spoke to me more or less as follows: 'I (Kristl) don't understand why playwrights, when they make a dramatic adaptation of the circumstances and consequences of a crime, almost always pick on so-called capital crimes, which are relatively rarely committed and hardly ever bother with minor crimes of the sort you encounter by the thousand the length and breadth of the country, the circumstances of which are as often as not shrouded in ignorance, but the consequences of which, in terms of loss of civil rights, nevertheless equally often resemble those following a life sentence or even a death sentence.'

And Kristl told me about a case he had come across – and this everyday case was the origin of the little dance of death *Faith, Hope and Charity*. The characters of Elisabeth, the policeman (Alfons Klostermeyer), the magistrate's wife and the chief inspector, Kristl knew personally. So I need to thank him here for making available his raw material and for a great deal of stimulation.

Kristl's intention was to write a play against the irresponsibly bureaucratic application of minor regulations – naturally in the knowledge that there will always be minor regulations, because there must be in any community however constituted. So in the end Kristl's intention was to articulate the hope that these minor regulations might (if you'll forgive a harsh expression) perhaps be more humanely applied.

Which was also my intention, or certainly I was clear in my mind that this anti-minor-regulations theme would undoubtedly provide the material to be able to portray once again the gigantic struggle between the individual and society, this eternal battle with no peaceful outcome – during which the individual can at best enjoy for a few moments the illusion of a ceasefire.

As with all my plays, I have made a great effort with this little dance of death not to forget that this, the individual's hopeless struggle, is fuelled by animal instinct and that therefore the problem of whether this struggle is pursued by heroic or cowardly means may be considered merely as a formal aspect of animality, which as we know is neither good nor evil.

As in all my plays I have on this occasion neither prettified nor disfigured. Whoever makes a conscientious attempt to characterize us human beings must undoubtedly acknowledge (unless his grasp of human nature is slight) that our expressions of feeling are tainted with kitsch, that is to say falsified, euphemistic, masochistically lusting for sympathy, no doubt as a result of a lazy-minded need to be accepted – and so whoever tries to characterize human beings honestly will always be confined to building mirrors, and here I would like to take the opportunity briefly to emphasize the following: I have never built and will never build distorting mirrors, because I reject parody in all its forms.

As in all my plays I have also tried on this occasion to be as disrespectful as possible towards stupidity and lies, on the grounds that this disrespectfulness might well respresent the principal duty of a literary artist who sometimes imagines his only motive for writing is to allow people to recognize themselves. Please recognize yourself! So that you may acquire that cheerfulness which will alleviate your own life-and-death struggle by virtue of the fact that a dose of honesty places you certainly not above yourself (for that would be conceited) but next to and below yourself, so that in spite of everything you are able to contemplate yourself not from on high, but from in front, behind, sideways and from underneath!

Any one of my plays could be called 'Faith, Hope and Charity'. And the following passage from the Bible could stand as epigraph to any one of my plays:

> And the LORD smelled a sweet savour; and the LORD said in his heart, I will not again curse the ground any more for man's sake; for the imagination of man's heart is evil from his youth; neither will I again smite any more every thing living, as I have done.
>
> While the earth remaineth, seedtime and harvest, and cold and heat, and summer and winter, and day and night shall not cease.
>
> Genesis, 8, xxi–xxii

ÖDÖN VON HORVÁTH

Translator's Note

Faith, Hope and Charity is pared down and chiselled from a mass of frequently fascinating material eventually rejected by Horváth. I have, with one exception, respected this impressive self-discipline. Among the papers relating to the play is a single sheet headed 'Monolog der Elisabeth'. In Heribert Sasse's Berlin production this speech, delivered by the actress as she moved through the auditorium, opened the play. In the summer of 1989, the Horváth archive came up for sale at Sotheby's (where it failed to make its reserve) and I was able to find the sheet of paper in question. Scrawled on it in red crayon was the indication that the speech was intended for Act Two. This may refer to an Act Two from an earlier draft (scenes in the zoo, back at Elisabeth's home and next to a sports car on the side of a country road were all, in various drafts, known as Act Two), but the speech (which begins 'It's nearly eight months . . .' on page 60 and ends '. . . the best way to get a job.') seemed to me to sit very well at the end of the present Act Two. I have omitted one or two phrases (including, for example, a reference to a character no longer in the play) and changed some tenses to fit the context; otherwise the whole speech has been translated. Purists may omit it: but I feel that apart from being touching and beautifully written, it provides at a distance of fifty years, valuable background which a contemporary audience might not have found necessary. Perhaps Horváth was afraid it might seem self-pitying: Heribert and I decided the risk was worth taking.

I should like, once again, to thank Ian Huish for his invaluable help and advice.

C.H.

Faith, Hope and Charity was first performed on 27 October 1989 at the Lyric Theatre, Hammersmith. The play was directed by Heribert Sasse and designed by Santiago del Corral.

Characters

Elisabeth
A Policeman (Alfons Klostermeyer)
Chief Dissector
Dissector
Assistant Dissector
The Baron in Mourning
Irene Prantl
The Magistrate's Wife
Himself, the Magistrate
A Disabled Veteran
A Worker's Wife
A Bookkeeper
Maria
A detective
The Chief Inspector
Second Policeman
Third Policeman
Joachim, the Daring Young Lifesaver

Act One

Scene One

The setting: in front of the Anatomical Institute, with its frosted glass windows.
Elisabeth *wants to go in and is looking around questioningly, but there's not a soul to be seen.*

In the distance a band intones Chopin's much-loved Funeral March, and now a young
Policeman *(Alfons Klostermeyer) strolls slowly past* **Elisabeth**, *apparently scarcely noticing her.*

It's springtime.

Scene Two

Elisabeth *speaks to the* **Policeman** *all of a sudden, as the sound of the Funeral March fades into the distance.*

Elisabeth   Excuse me . . . it's just I'm looking for the Anatomy.

Policeman   The Anatomical Institute?

Elisabeth   Where they cut up the corpses.

Policeman   This is it, that there.

Elisabeth   That's all right then.

Silence.

Policeman   *(smiling)* You take care, miss . . . there's heads in there, stacked up in rows.

Elisabeth   I'm not afraid of dead bodies.

Policeman   Me neither.

Elisabeth   It's been a long time since I've been frightened of anything.

Policeman   Likewise . . .

A light gesture of farewell and he's gone.

Scene Three

Elisabeth *watches the* **Policeman** *go, her expression ironic . . . then she plucks up courage and presses the bell of the Anatomical Institute. We hear it ring, inside, and then the* **Dissector** *appears in his white coat. He stands in the doorway, staring at the apparently indecisive* **Elisabeth**.

Scene Four

Dissector   What do you want?

Elisabeth   I'd like to see someone in authority.

Dissector   In what connection?

Elisabeth   It's quite urgent.

Dissector   Are we looking after a corpse for you? A loved one?

Elisabeth   It's not to do with a corpse, it's to do with me personally.

Dissector   Whatever do you mean?

Elisabeth   Are you in a position of authority here?

Dissector   I'm the Dissector, you can rely on me.

Silence.

Elisabeth   The thing is, I was told quite particularly, you could sell your body here . . . what I mean is, once I'm dead, the people in there could do what they like with my body in the cause of science . . . but in the meantime I get the fee for it paid out. Right now.

Dissector   New one on me.

Elisabeth   But I was told quite particularly.

Dissector   Who by?

Elisabeth   Someone at work.

Dissector   What's your job, then?

Elisabeth   I don't really have anything just at the moment. It'll be worse before it's better. But I never let it get me down.

Silence.

Dissector   Selling your own corpse . . . what's the world coming to?

Elisabeth   Beggars can't be choosers.

Dissector   Ludicrous idea . . .

*He takes a bag of birdseed out of his pocket and feeds the pigeons, which fly down from the roof of the Anatomical Institute . . . the pigeons know the **Dissector** well and perch on his shoulder and eat out of his hand.*

Scene Five

*Now the **Chief Dissector** shows a **Baron** with a black armband out of the Anatomical Institute into the fresh air.*

Chief Dissector   Soon to be out of the way, Baron; and once again, my deepest sympathy.

Baron   Thank you, doctor. I blame myself, you know.

Chief Dissector   But the Public Prosecutor's Inquiry established the absolute insubstantiality of every single charge raised against you. All of us are in God's hands.

Baron   All the same: I was at Verdun and in the battle of the Somme, but nothing's ever affected me as much as that accident yesterday. We'd only been married for three months and I was driving . . . round that blind corner. Just between Lechbruch and Steingaden. Good thing they released the corpse.

Meanwhile, the **Chief Dissector** *has noticed the* **Dissector**.

Chief Dissector   One moment, if you'd be so kind. (*He comes right up to the* **Dissector**, *screaming at him.*) Are you feeding those pigeons again? What do you think you're doing? This isn't a pigsty! There are fingers and pharynxes lying about all over the place! There are those hearts to be finished off, both of them *and* the remains of that spleen, if you'd be so kind! God help us all, it's chaos in there!

Dissector   But this young lady was wanting to sell us her corpse, you see . . .

Chief Dissector   Her corpse? What, again?

Silence.

Baron   Extraordinary.

Chief Dissector   God knows how many times we've had to deny that we buy dead people when they're alive, doesn't anyone ever listen to official announcements? They get some idea, the state's going to pay out something for their body . . . what makes them think they're that interesting? The state, they think the state should take care of everything.

Baron   A quite extraordinary view of the responsibilities of the state.

Chief Dissector   Things are going to change any minute, Baron.

Baron   Let's hope so.

Scene Six

The **Assistant Dissector** *hurriedly emerges from the Anatomical Institute with the* **Chief Dissector**'s *hat.*

Assistant Dissector   Telephone, sir.

Chief Dissector   What, for me?

Assistant Dissector   It's something to do with the verdict in the Leopoldine Hackinger case. The woman from Brno. You're supposed to go and see the Professor at the clinic right away . . .

He hands him his hat.

Chief Dissector   Right away!

*He scrambles out of his white coat and hands it to the **Assistant Dissector**, who vanishes back into the Anatomical Institute: then turns to the **Baron**.*

Excuse me, Baron. Some woman from the Sudetenland: the experts can't seem to work out what it is she's died of. Duty calls . . .

Baron   Well, of course.

Chief Dissector   . . . and once again, my deepest sympathy.

Baron   Well, thank you.

Chief Dissector   It's been a privilege.

He exits right, moving fast.

Baron   Bye . . .

He exits left, moving slowly; and once again, far in the distance, a few phrases from Chopin's Funeral March. The light gradually begins to fade, as it's already late afternoon.

Scene Seven

*The **Dissector** watches the **Chief Dissector** leave.*

Dissector   Not a nice man. Poor pigeons. You want my advice, miss: best thing you can do is go home and throw yourself out the window.

Elisabeth   Well, you are a help.

Dissector   I'm trying to do you a favour. Who's going to buy a corpse? Nowadays?

Elisabeth   Tomorrow is another day.

Dissector   Nothing changes.

Elisabeth   I don't believe that.

Dissector   Oh, you don't?

Silence. **Elisabeth** *smiles.*

Elisabeth   No . . . I'm not going to let you convince me my luck won't change. Listen, suppose I'd been able to sell my corpse for let's say a hundred and fifty marks . . .

Dissector   (*interrupting her*) A hundred and fifty marks?

Elisabeth   That's right.

The **Dissector** *grins.*

Dissector   You're like a child . . .

Elisabeth   Why do you say that?

Dissector   What's your father do?

Elisabeth   He's an inspector.

Dissector   An inspector? Well, well!

Elisabeth   But he can't support me just at the moment, because my mum passed away in March and he's had a lot of expense.

Dissector   What's a humble chief dissector compared to an inspector? Well, well, miss!

Elisabeth   See, if I had a hundred and fifty marks, I could get my sales permit and then there's no knowing what I could do . . . because with my sales permit I could start tomorrow, I could find a more or less self-supporting job in my original line I got thrown out of because of the Depression.

Silence.

Dissector   What sort of line was that, then?

Elisabeth   Girdles, corsetry. Wholesale. And bras, all that sort of thing.

Dissector   Interesting.

Silence.

Elisabeth   Where is the life that once I knew?

Silence. The **Dissector** *fumbles with his wallet and fetches out a photograph.*

Dissector   Have a look at this . . .

Elisabeth *contemplates the photograph.*

Elisabeth   Nice dog.

Dissector   Little terrier . . .

Elisabeth   Intelligent looking.

Dissector   And snappy! Unfortunately, he handed in his dinner pail.

Elisabeth   Shame.

The **Dissector** *whistles.*

Dissector   That was his whistle. He'd always come. (*He addresses the photograph.*) Good boy, you're gone now, aren't you, my good boy . . . no more walkies . . . (*He puts the photograph away and turns to* **Elisabeth**.) It's really nice of you to be so sympathetic about my poor old chap. What's your Christian name?

Elisabeth   Elisabeth.

Silence.

Dissector   Empress Elisabeth of Austria, there's another gallant little woman . . . didn't stop terrorists picking her off. In Geneva. Where the League of Nations is . . . and that's another racket! I still have my butterfly collection and a canary; and a cat made friends with me yesterday. Are you interested in aquaria?

Elisabeth   What?

Dissector   I've got a terrarium as well.

Elisabeth   Terrarium sounds even better.

Dissector   Well, then you must come and pay me a visit.

Elisabeth   Maybe.

Scene Eight

Now the **Chief Dissector**, *on his way back from the clinic, makes a somewhat surprising entrance: his finger is thickly bandaged. He observes the* **Dissector**, *stopping indignantly and staring at him, as he makes to move away, while* **Elisabeth** *also withdraws.*

Scene Nine

The **Chief Dissector** *slowly approaches the* **Dissector** *and stops right in front of him.*

Chief Dissector   What again? Are you still feeding those pigeons? (*He suddenly lets fly at him.*) Will you make yourself scarce! (*He turns to* **Elisabeth**.) Is that understood?

Elisabeth   Yes.

She goes.

Scene Ten

The **Chief Dissector** *watches* **Elisabeth** *leave.*

Chief Dissector   Well, this is just what the doctor ordered. I thought you might be cataloguing those tumours at last, not standing around entertaining the weaker sex.

Dissector   That's where you are wrong. Her father is a government inspector fallen on hard times.

Chief Dissector   A government inspector?

Dissector   That's right. And if she could get a hundred and fifty marks, she'd have her sales permit and there's no knowing what she could do . . . I know you think I'm incompetent, just because I have an aquarium and I feed the pigeons and I'm kind-hearted . . .

Chief Dissector   Get to the point.

Dissector   The point is I'm going to take this government inspector's daughter under my wing and support her. I've made up my mind. A hundred and fifty marks.

Chief Dissector   A hundred and fifty?

Dissector   She'll pay me back.

Chief Dissector   I think you're an impulsive party who still believes in miracles. If you were my wife, I'd beat your head in . . .

He threatens him roguishly with his thickly bandaged finger.

Dissector   What's wrong with your finger? Hurt yourself?

Chief Dissector   An infection.

Dissector   Not from a corpse?

Chief Dissector   Where else? Just now. That tricky case from Brno.

Dissector   You want to be careful of that, sir.

Silence. The **Chief Dissector** *considers his thickly bandaged finger.*

Chief Dissector   It doesn't hurt; that's funny . . .

Dissector   Whenever I consider my butterfly collection, for example, I always think everything is organized according to some higher plan.

Chief Dissector   You're rambling again: come along, duty calls!

He exits with the **Dissector** *into the Anatomical Institute. Darkness.*

Act Two

Scene One

The setting: the office in Irene Prantl's shop. **Irene Prantl** *is a garrulous woman, particularly in her professional life. At the moment she's at her desk, busy with her accounts, looking very important. In front of her sits a* **Magistrate's Wife**. *In the background, wax dummies wearing corsets, girdles, brassières and so on . . . stacked up in rows, like the heads in the Anatomical Institute.*

Prantl   I really have to take my hat off to you! Seven girdles, six corsets and eleven pairs of suspenders in three days flat . . . congratulations! You've got the knack! Better than most of the professionals! Real talent!

Magistrate's Wife   Well, goodness, as a magistrate's wife, I move in certain social circles, acquaintances, you know, who scarcely want to be seen turning me down . . .

Prantl   No, you're too modest! It's not a piece of cake these days, selling, people slam the door in your face!

Magistrate's Wife   But I insist on our agreement: if anyone asks, naturally you'll say I'm only selling these things as a sort of hobby . . .

Prantl   Goes without saying, it'll be our secret!

Magistrate's Wife   Times are hard when you have to support your own husband, *and* he's earning over six hundred marks. People are being laid off left, right and centre, not the county-court judges of course or the top civil servants . . .

She breaks off as the telephone rings. **Prantl** *answers it.*

Prantl   Yes. Send her in . . . one second, if you don't mind, this won't take a minute.

Scene Two

Elisabeth *enters.*

Good morning, come in, let's have a look . . . Where's your book of words?

Elisabeth   Here.

She hands over her order book. **Prantl** *leafs through it.*

Prantl   What? Two pairs of suspenders, a girdle and a corset, you might as well not bother!

Elisabeth   It's not a piece of cake these days, selling, people slam the door in your face.

Prantl No need to be vulgar! Your job as a saleswoman is to develop the customer's feeling for beauty! The whole country's exercise-mad now, you see naked women everywhere, what could be better publicity for our lines? And you've got to pay more attention to our lords and masters, I've never met a man yet who wasn't interested in suspender belts! How did you do in Kaufbeuren?

Elisabeth I didn't do anything in Kaufbeuren.

Prantl What do you mean? Kaufbeuren's always been astronomical!

Elisabeth But I didn't get to Kaufbeuren.

Prantl Why not?

Elisabeth I wanted to save time, so I got a lift, straight there as the crow flies . . . but all of a sudden the car broke down and I had to spend the night in a barn in the forest.

Prantl *lets fly at her.*

Prantl In the forest? What do you think I'm paying you for? If that's the way the crow flies, it'll be Judgement Day before you work off that hundred and fifty marks I advanced you for your sales permit!

Elisabeth It was an act of God.

Prantl When my employees start in with acts of God, it's all over as far as I'm concerned! That's when I cut my throat! Blood-poisoning or falling out of the train and breaking a leg, that I can just about wear, but Irene Prantl has never yet surrendered to the luxury of an act of God!

Elisabeth There's nothing I can do about it.

Prantl And don't look so pained, little Miss Act of God! Just look at this lady! She's married to a magistrate, she doesn't need a job, it's purely a hobby and she's done four times your turnover.

Scene Three

The **Dissector** *bursts in and immediately lets fly at* **Elisabeth**. *He's beside himself.*

Dissector There you are, you impostor! You swindler! Your father's not a government inspector. He's just some claims inspector in an insurance office. If you hadn't told me he was a government inspector, do you think I'd have provided for you like that?

Elisabeth I never said anything of the sort . . .

Dissector (*interrupting her*) Yes, you did, that's exactly what you said!

Elisabeth No! Never!

The **Dissector** *smashes his walking stick down on* **Prantl***'s desk, scattering papers and bellowing.*

Dissector   Government inspector! You said government inspector!

Prantl *rescues her papers, shrieking.*

Prantl   Stop it!

Silence. The **Dissector** *bows chivalrously to* **Prantl** *and the* **Magistrate's Wife.**

Dissector   Do excuse me, ladies, out of a clear blue sky, but compared to a claims inspector, even a humble chief dissector is a person of some authority and this dangerous woman has inveigled good money out of me . . .

Elisabeth   (*interrupting him*) It's just not true!

Prantl   Be quiet!

Dissector   Be quiet!

Prantl *waves a threatening finger.*

Prantl   Now, now, miss . . . a raised voice is a sure sign of guilt.

Dissector   (*raising his voice*) Guilt! That's right!

Silence.

Elisabeth   I won't say another word.

Dissector   (*malevolently*) That'd just suit you, wouldn't it?

Prantl   (*to the* **Dissector**) Please sit down.

Dissector   Thank you . . . (*He sits down.*) I'm a very kind-hearted man, but I will not tolerate being lied to.

Elisabeth   I never lied to you.

Prantl   Will you stop interrupting . . .

Dissector   Yes, thank you.

Prantl *offers the* **Dissector** *a cigarette.*

Prantl   Do you?

Dissector   Yes, I'll take the liberty . . . (*He lights up, settles himself comfortably, exhaling voluptuously.*) So, ladies . . . she comes to my flat, she takes advantage of my paternal instincts, I show her my aquarium and lend her my book on Tibet and over and above all that I pay for her sales permit . . . and all the time her father isn't a government inspector! I made inquiries, just to put my mind at rest, because my colleagues are always making fun of my soft-heartedness.

Prantl   Sales permit? What sales permit? She got that from me.

Dissector   What? You as well?

Prantl It's company policy. The firm offers it to employees in the form of an optional advance which they can work off. A hundred and fifty marks.

Dissector (*beside himself*) A hundred and fifty marks?

Prantl That's fraud.

Elisabeth *suddenly lets fly.*

Elisabeth I am not a criminal!

Magistrate's Wife That's not what matters, miss, your opinion. Whether there's material evidence of fraud, that's what matters. Otherwise justice would grind to a halt.

Prantl Quite right.

Magistrate's Wife It's none of my business and personally I thank God I have nothing to do with the law except that I happen to be married to a judge. But if you didn't use this gentleman's money to buy your sales permit, then . . . my August would say, I can hear him now: misrepresentation of the facts . . . material evidence of fraud.

The **Dissector** *has slumped despairingly.*

Dissector (*lachrymose*) I'm only a poor dissector who tried to do a good deed . . .

Elisabeth You'll get your money back.

Dissector No.

Elisabeth Yes, you will, every penny.

Dissector When?

Elisabeth I'll work it off.

Prantl Oh? How? (*She reads from* **Elisabeth***'s order book.*) Two pairs of suspenders, a girdle and a corset. And an act of God.

Dissector (*exploding*) 'Act of God'? Fraud! Give me my money back this minute!

Elisabeth I haven't got it.

Prantl But I gave you your sales permit.

Elisabeth That's true.

Dissector Well, then!

Elisabeth I needed the money this man lent me for something more urgent.

Prantl Curiouser and curiouser!

Elisabeth It was personal. I needed it to pay a fine.

The **Dissector** *is beside himself again.*

Dissector   What? You've already had a brush with the law? You've got a previous conviction? I'll put you in gaol for this, I promise you that! I was your last victim! (*He storms out.*)

Scene Four

Prantl   Wonderful! That's wonderful!

Magistrate's Wife   If that gentleman testifies under oath about the government inspector and the claims inspector, they'll find you guilty.

Prantl   Gaol.

Magistrate's Wife   But don't worry. Only prison, that's all. And not more than fourteen days.

Elisabeth   Everyone'll think I'm some arch-criminal.

Prantl   You can't stop people thinking, especially seeing as you kept quiet about your previous conviction.

Elisabeth   I'm under no obligation to tell you anything.

Prantl   Don't be so superior! This scandal is a disgrace. Naturally you're dismissed at once . . . but now you wait here, while I fetch the police. (*She exits.*)

Scene Five

Magistrate's Wife   It's none of my business, but a previous conviction always looks bad.

Elisabeth *recites her answer like a schoolgirl.*

Elisabeth   I have a previous conviction because I once worked without a sales permit . . . so they slapped a hundred and fifty mark fine on me, payable in instalments. But eventually it all came due and I would have had to go to prison and I'd have gone under . . . so I used the dissector's money to pay my fine. It's nearly eight months since I was made redundant . . . and I had to clear out of my room and pawn my brooch . . . I tried sharing with a friend, we didn't get on but I never let it get me down. So I went on my travels and they said things were getting better and there'd be jobs again, otherwise there'd be riots and revolution. Except I couldn't find a job and there was no revolution, but I never let it get me down. And people stayed calm and kept their mouths shut, or if they didn't, they were locked up . . . and when I looked at the Situations Wanted in the paper my stomach turned over, but I never let it get me down. And in the paper it talked about the misery of the people and the Minister said the state is a welfare state and that that was the whole trouble. Undermined morale and killed initiative and so on and so forth. And I found out how difficult it was to get on with other people. But I never let it get me down. And you were cheated and exploited everywhere, at least you were if you had nothing. So I said to the state: 'Listen, I'm a citizen too,' but the state didn't answer. And then I found this job, but to get it I needed money. A genuine job as a saleswoman . . . and I needed a deposit of a hundred and fifty marks. Well, I wasn't going to let that get me down! I still believe my luck is bound to change . . . it's the only faith I have left. And faith moves mountains and I'm not going to let anything get me down. I spent my last bit of money on make-up: it's still the best way to get a job.

Silence.

Magistrate's Wife All you have to remember is don't keep denying everything and don't pretend to be cleverer than the judge. My husband's a good man, but don't let the defence drag the case out just for the sake of it. If I'm sitting at home with his lunch waiting for him and he can't get away because the sitting's going on so long, that's when he starts to get unreasonable . . . You see, the accused needs to have some consideration as well, after all, a judge is only human.

Darkness.

Act Three

Scene One

The setting: in front of the Social Security Office with its minimal front garden.

A group of clients of the Social Security Office are having a discussion; a **Worker's Wife,** *an elderly* **Bookkeeper** *and a young woman called* **Maria. Elisabeth** *is there too. She's leaning against the garden railings, catching some watery late afternoon sun. Now, a disabled* **Veteran** *hobbles out of the Social Security Office.*

Scene Two

Veteran   Well, three cheers! Now the Social Security turn round and say it's not their responsibility, I'm supposed to be somewhere else . . . Bloody hell!

Worker's Wife   You'll be wanting the Pensions Office.

Veteran   Pensions Office says, it's nothing to do with them, it's a National Insurance matter. Insurance says, my feet was already done in before the accident, because of my varicose veins and fallen arches . . . and their tame expert says to my face I could've been walking about without a stick for years if I put my mind to it!

Bookkeeper   Have you tried the Appeals Tribunal?

Veteran   All they did was agreed the National Insurance could cut my money down from 60 percent to 40 . . . they stuck an extra paragraph on my arbitration, saying the plaintiff had no incentive to look for a job, because when he was working, he was not earning significantly more than he is from his pension!

Scene Three

Now everyone falls silent and remains motionless, while a **Policeman** *(Alfons Klostermeyer) strolls slowly by, apparently taking no notice of anyone. Already the light is gradually beginning to fade.*

Scene Four

The **Worker's Wife** *watches the* **Policeman** *leave.*

Worker's Wife   There goes the general . . .

Bookkeeper   Give us this day our daily bread.

Maria My problem's even worse.

Veteran How come?

Maria There's seven in my family and the eighth is on the way . . . but because my father's bringing home forty marks a week, they've started making stoppages.

Veteran It's all a racket.

Elisabeth They wouldn't give me anything, because my father's still earning.

Bookkeeper What's he do, your father?

Elisabeth Claims inspector in an insurance office. I'm sorry, I have to laugh . . . (*She laughs.*)

Worker's Wife What are you laughing at, you silly cow? (**Elisabeth** *stops laughing abruptly.*) All you have to do is go home.

Elisabeth No!

Worker's Wife Then it's your own fault. If your father's an inspector . . .

Elisabeth (*interrupting her*) Claims inspector in an insurance office!

Worker's Wife Same difference!

Elisabeth (*grinning*) Is it?

Bookkeeper A fool and his pride are never parted.

Worker's Wife A home to go to and won't take advantage!

Elisabeth There's good reason for it.

Worker's Wife Have you done something wrong?

Elisabeth *smiles uncertainly.*

Elisabeth Does it show?

Silence. The **Bookkeeper** *grins.*

Bookkeeper All that glisters is not gold . . . (*He exits.*)

Scene Five

Maria (*to* **Elisabeth**) You just have to learn to put up with it.

Elisabeth I don't want to talk about it.

Scene Six

The **Veteran** *counts on his fingers, talking to himself.*

Veteran   Social Security Office. Job Centre. National Insurance. Pensions Office. Appeals Tribunal . . . see you in the mass grave! (*He exits.*)

Scene Seven

Worker's Wife   (*to herself*) The mass grave . . . that's how long you have to wait before they take care of you. (*She exits.*)

Scene Eight

Maria   What you do wrong?

Elisabeth   Nothing.

Maria   Did they lock you up? (**Elisabeth** *doesn't answer.*) Don't worry, you can tell me . . . I know how it goes. It's only some pissy little rule, but you get caught . . . You don't really know what you've done, but it's all over. Listen, they threw my father inside for ten days because he brought home a couple of planks from the building site . . . they were just lying around and our roof was leaking, rain coming in on the beds. If you do something wrong, you'd better be sure it's really worthwhile.

Elisabeth *still doesn't answer. It's dark now and the two women are alone, perching on the base of the railings, lit by the light streaming out of the windows of the Social Security Office.*

Ever been married?

Elisabeth   No. (*Silence.*) See, my father and I are different sorts of people. I mean, when I was born, he was furious I was only a girl. And he went on holding it against me. On the other hand he makes out he's a man of the world. If my mother was alive, she could tell you a few sad stories. Men are all selfish bastards.

Maria   You just haven't found the right one.

Elisabeth   Maybe.

Maria   He'll come out of the blue. Just when you least expect it.

Silence.

Elisabeth   I like one man in every ten thousand, at the most.

Maria   Well, yes.

Elisabeth   I've always wanted to be independent . . . you know, my own master.

Maria   Never works. (*Silence.*) I got nothing against getting married. Long as he didn't beat me . . . What you doing now?

Elisabeth   Nothing.

Silence.

Maria   You can call me Maria.

Elisabeth   All right.

Silence. Suddenly **Maria** *gets up.*

Maria   Come on! Let's see what we can do . . . there's a bloke over there, he'll buy us a ham roll.

Elisabeth   No, I don't want to.

Silence.

Maria   Why not?

Elisabeth   No. Self-preservation.

Silence.

Maria   Pull the other one, it's got bells on . . .

Scene Nine

Now the **Baron** *with the black armband appears . . . he looks somewhat battered, tired and embittered.* **Maria** *catches sight of him and stares at him, fascinated.*

Scene Ten

The **Baron** *bows gallantly.*

Baron   Good evening, my dear. I was afraid you might not put in an appearance.

Maria   (*tonelessly*) I said I would.

Silence. The **Baron** *recognizes* **Elisabeth**.

Baron   Ah!

He raises his hat and smiles maliciously.

Maria   Oh? You know my friend from out of town?

Baron   Out of town? (*To* **Elisabeth**.) You're the one who wanted to sell your valuable corpse, aren't you?

Maria   Corpse?

The **Baron** *slides off his somewhat crumpled armband.*

Baron   Yes, those were the days. I had my own business then . . .

Elisabeth *grins.*

Elisabeth   Corsets, was it?

Baron   No, liquor. Now I'm broke.

Maria *is looking at herself in the hand mirror, in the light from the Social Security Office.*

Maria   Hugo! Notice anything different?

Baron   I can't quite put my finger on it.

Maria   There . . . (*She shows her teeth.*) I had them crowned the day before yesterday, these two front ones . . . see, these two used to be all black and broken down, the nerves were dead.

The **Baron** *smiles cunningly.*

Baron   You've improved your prospects.

Maria   Pleased to hear it.

Scene Eleven

Now a **Detective** *appears, behind* **Maria**, *who is still inspecting her crowns in the hand mirror. The* **Baron** *withdraws somewhat and the* **Detective** *waits until* **Maria** *turns round. Now she notices him and starts.*

Scene Twelve

Detective   You come with me. You know why.

Maria   (*subdued*) No, I don't.

Detective   Oh, so you don't . . .

Baron   Where are my cufflinks?

Silence.

Maria   (*quietly*) Jesus Christ.

Baron   Who do you think stole them?

Detective   I'm a police officer. Come with me.

Maria *stares at the* **Baron**.

Maria You turned me in.

Detective You keep your mouth shut.

Maria You did. And I lent you three marks. Three marks!

Detective Shut up.

Another gallant bow from the **Baron**.

Baron Good evening, my dear. (*He exits.*)

Maria You pig, you shit!

The **Detective** *swiftly handcuffs her.*

Detective Shut up! Move! (*He drags her off.*)

Maria Ow!

Scene Thirteen

The **Policeman** *(Alfons Klostermeyer) hurries up towards the sound of the disturbance, stops and looks at* **Elisabeth**.

Scene Fourteen

Policeman What's all this, then?

Elisabeth *smiles maliciously.*

Elisabeth Nothing. Just a woman being arrested. For no reason.

Policeman No, they wouldn't do that.

Elisabeth All the same.

Silence.

Why are you staring at me?

Policeman (*smiling*) Is there a law against it? (*Silence.*) The thing is you remind me of someone. Your general demeanour. One of the dear departed.

Elisabeth You're very mysterious.

Silence.

Policeman Which way are you going?

Elisabeth Do you want to walk me home?

Policeman I'm off duty.

Elisabeth I'd rather go on my own.

Policeman (*with no ulterior motive*) Don't you like the police?

Elisabeth (*starting somewhat*) Why do you say that?

Policeman   Because you don't want me to walk you home. There have to be police, miss! I mean, deep in every one of us there's a mass murderer.

Elisabeth   Not in me.

Policeman   Go on, there's no such thing!

Elisabeth   (*imitating him*) 'There's no such thing!'

Policeman   (*smiling*) You're behaving like someone that's been condemned to death.

Elisabeth   Not that anyone would give a damn.

Policeman   Hope springs eternal.

Elisabeth   That's just a saying.

Silence.

Policeman   Without faith, hope and charity, how could life go on? It all connects logically.

Elisabeth   It's all very well for you to say that, you're an official, your position is secure.

Policeman   We all have to die.

Elisabeth   Don't talk to me about charity!

Silence.

Policeman   Listen, miss. Just listen to me for a minute . . . I've been watching you here in front of the Social Security Office for days now. Because you remind me of someone . . . like I said, one of the dear departed.

Elisabeth   Who was this dear departed?

Policeman   My fiancée. (*Silence.*) We were like this. But she had something up with her liver and now I really miss her. What's so funny?

Elisabeth   Nothing.

Silence.

Policeman   You seem very bitter.

Elisabeth   I'm a fast walker.

Policeman   You walk as fast as you like, I'll keep up with you.

A shot rings out in the distance . . . then another and another; somebody cries out. Silence. The **Policeman** *listens.*

What was that? Sounds as if they're shooting at each other again. There'll be civil war soon, it's just insanity . . . I'll just go and have a look, be right back, wait for me.

Elisabeth   All right.

The **Policeman** *exits right.*

Scene Fifteen

Now the **Magistrate's Wife** *and himself, the* **Magistrate**, *enter left.*

Magistrate's Wife   This way, August! And in you go to the Social Security Office and tell the Privy Counsellor you're afraid you can't be at his disposal this evening, because you're promised to your better half.

Magistrate   But you know I don't like going to the cinema. No cigars for two hours.

Magistrate's Wife   Does you good! Remember your bowels!

Magistrate   I know. The doctor warned me about them only yesterday.

Magistrate's Wife   He warned me as well, he told me I shouldn't climb steps with my glands . . .

Magistrate   (*interrupting her*) Then why do you have to sell corsets? Complete lunacy!

Magistrate's Wife   I don't want to have to come crawling on my knees for every penny!

Magistrate   It's wrong to exaggerate! What do you know about real poverty? You don't have to sentence poor people day in and day out, whose only real crime is not having a roof over their head.

Magistrate's Wife   In that case, I wouldn't sentence them.

Magistrate   Hermine! (*Silence.*) So. Now I have to tell the Privy Counsellor that our cribbage game is up the spout, because I'm promised to my better half . . . but if your film's another dud, you'd better watch out, Mickey Mouse . . .

He exits into the Social Security Office.

Scene Sixteen

Now the **Magistrate's Wife** *looks at* **Elisabeth**. *They stare at each other, but* **Elisabeth** *no longer wants to know anyone from her past . . . however, the* **Magistrate's Wife** *won't give way.*

Scene Seventeen

Magistrate's Wife   Funny. We've met . . .

Elisabeth *looks around, frightened.*

Elisabeth   Please don't recognize me . . .

Magistrate's Wife   Don't be afraid! It's none of my business, but how long did you get?

Elisabeth   Fourteen days.

Magistrate's Wife   See, that's exactly what I told you.

Elisabeth   And no remission.

Magistrate's Wife   No?

Elisabeth   Because I had a previous conviction when they fined me . . . (*She grins.*) If I knew what I'd done wrong . . .

Magistrate's Wife   Yes, I know how it happens! You don't have to tell me! Plain injustice . . . and I suppose you haven't been able to find a new job?

Elisabeth   No. But I met a man just now and he told me about the death of his fiancée . . . (*She grins again.*)

Magistrate's Wife   No question it'd be the best thing for you: marriage.

Elisabeth   (*tonelessly*) I wouldn't say no.

Magistrate's Wife   Well, congratulations.

Elisabeth   We met purely by chance.

Magistrate's Wife   Always the same. And I know. I know!

Elisabeth   Maybe it's my big chance.

Magistrate's Wife   What's he do, your intended?

Elisabeth   He's an official.

Magistrate's Wife   An official? Does he know about the fourteen days?

Elisabeth   No.

Magistrate's Wife   Ah. Well, you must tell him, otherwise it might eventually cause him difficulties in his career . . .

Elisabeth   Is that possible?

Magistrate's Wife   Absolutely.

Elisabeth   There he is, he's coming back.

Magistrate's Wife   Where? . . . What, a policeman? . . . Well, it's nothing to do with me. Good luck. (*She moves away from her.*)

Scene Eighteen

*The **Policeman** reappears, speaks to **Elisabeth**.*

Policeman   Well, I'm free now. Some passer-by got shot. Why should we have to live in times like these, that's what I often think. (*Suddenly, he points at the **Magistrate's Wife**.*) That woman, what'd she want?

Elisabeth   (*lying*) I don't know her.

Policeman   It's just she's staring at us.

Elisabeth   Perhaps she's mixing us up. It's easy to mix people up.

Policeman   That's true. On the other hand, if I as a respresentative of state authority were to mix two people up . . . well, it wouldn't be good for my career.

Elisabeth   Are they really that strict?

Policeman   Very. And often it's completely unjust. Are you cold, is that why your teeth are chattering?

Elisabeth   Yes.

Policeman   Very?

Elisabeth   Quite.

Policeman   I'd happily give you my coat, I certainly don't need it, but it's not allowed.

Elisabeth   (*smiling*) Your coat's still on duty.

Policeman   Rules are rules.

Elisabeth   Come on, the wind's wicked . . .

*She exits slowly with the **Policeman**.*

Scene Nineteen

*Now the **Magistrate** emerges from the Social Security Office. His **Wife**'s tone is quite gossipy, all of a sudden.*

Magistrate's Wife   Listen, August . . . that's that girl from Prantl's over there, you know, that case of fraud about the claims inspector and the government inspector.

Magistrate   I don't know what you're talking about.

Magistrate's Wife   But you sentenced her . . .

Magistrate   It's quite possible.

Silence.

Magistrate's Wife   You should have given her some remission, though, I don't call that very just . . .

Magistrate   (*furious*) You worry about your own injustices, Hermine!

Darkness.

Act Four

Scene One

The setting: **Elisabeth***'s bed-sitting room.*

The **Policeman** *(Alfons Klostermeyer) lies in bed in his underpants, dozing.* **Elisabeth** *is brewing coffee, glancing from time to time at the white autumn asters which stand in a vase next to the primus stove.*
Outside, the October sun shines, but the curtains are half drawn and all in all it's a happy and peaceful image of domestic bliss.

Scene Two

Elisabeth *smells the white autumn asters.*

Elisabeth   What a long time they last. Five days already. When we first met I never imagined you'd buy me white asters.

Policeman   Soon as I saw them, some inner voice.

Elisabeth   All the same.

Policeman   What did you think, this dashing policeman's bound to be a fickle butterfly? On the lookout for a rich woman? Big mistake. Someone depends on me means much more to me than the other way round. What about another kiss?

Elisabeth   All right.

Policeman   Is the coffee nearly ready?

Elisabeth   Any minute.

The **Policeman** *takes some earphones from the bedside table and puts them on.*

Policeman   Attention! Very dashing . . .

He hums along with the Radetzky March, which is being played on the radio.

Elisabeth   Listen, Alfons . . . last night there was a wonderful opera broadcast. *Aida.*

The **Policeman** *puts the earphones back on the bedside table.*

Policeman   Weren't you missing me?

Elisabeth   Alfons!

Policeman   What about another kiss?

Elisabeth   Here's your coffee . . . (*She brings him a cup.*) And here's your kiss
. . . (*She kisses him and sits on the edge of the bed. The* **Policeman** *sips his coffee
pleasurably.*)

Policeman   Thank God we've got through to today. Constant state of
emergency . . . good thing the bloody elections are over. Night before last
another of my mates was shot.

Elisabeth   There's always been massacre of the innocents.

Policeman   Wouldn't happen if we had law and order.

Elisabeth   I can see there's always been injustices, because of man's
inhumanity to man . . . all you can hope for is a few less injustices.

Policeman   Never mind the philosophy. What d'you like most about me?

Elisabeth   Everything.

Policeman   But what word describes me best?

Elisabeth   I don't know.

Policeman   Go on, you must know.

Elisabeth   You've changed a bit, Alfons. You used to be sadder.

Policeman   What d'you mean?

Elisabeth   Well, more melancholy.

Policeman   Oh, I still am. Don't make me laugh!

Elisabeth   I'm sorry . . . (*She gets up.*)

Policeman   Where are you going? Oh, I see. Don't wrap a corset round
your feelings.

Elisabeth *flinches, speaks sharply.*

Elisabeth   What d'you mean, a corset?

Policeman   (*surprised*) Why?

Silence. **Elisabeth** *smiles.*

Elisabeth   I'm sorry, I'm a bit jumpy today . . . (*She leaves the room.*)

Scene Three

Policeman   (*alone*) . . . melancholy? More melancholy? . . . What d'you
mean, more melancholy?

Scene Four

Elisabeth *reappears.*

Policeman   You've been a long time.

Elisabeth   Have I?

Policeman   Nothing the matter, is there?

Elisabeth   I don't understand what you mean.

Policeman   I've always been very careful.

Elisabeth   Oh, I see.

Scene Five

There's a knock on the door. The lovers listen . . . but there's another knock, this time more decisive.

Policeman   Sh! No one at home.

Elisabeth   Who can it be?

Scene Six

Voice   Police!

Elisabeth   Jesus Christ!

Policeman   Police? And I'm stuck here. Yes, we have no bananas!

He hurriedly gathers up his clothes and hides in the wardrobe.

Scene Seven

The knocking at the door is even more decisive. **Elisabeth** *opens the door and a man steps into the bed-sitting room. He's a* **Chief Inspector** *from the Vice Squad.*

Chief Inspector   Everything comes to him who waits.

He looks around and points to the unmade bed.

I wake you up?

Elisabeth   Why?

Chief Inspector   You know why.

Elisabeth   I'm not feeling at my best today.

Chief Inspector   Now there are people who work all night, they tend to need a bit of rest during the day.

Elisabeth   I don't know what you mean.

The **Chief Inspector** *flourishes a suspender, which he's found on the chair.*

Chief Inspector   Hold your socks up with suspenders, do you?

Silence.

Elisabeth   What d'you want?

Chief Inspector   You received an employment order from the police, which states that within three weeks you would seek *certified* employment. But not only do you not have a job, there's no indication you've made any attempt to find one.

Elisabeth   Why don't you worry about the real unemployed?

Chief Inspector   I didn't come here for a political diatribe. Being unemployed is not contrary to police regulations, what's contrary to police regulations is being a threat to public order.

Elisabeth   But I'm not a threat to public order.

Chief Inspector   As long as you remain unable to give a satisfactory account of your earnings, that remains open to debate.

Elisabeth   I've been taken care of.

Chief Inspector   Precisely and it is the nature of this care which we're interested in.

Elisabeth   But I've explained that already. My fiancé gives me twenty marks a week. That's what I live on.

Chief Inspector   Who is he, this fiancé? (*Silence.*) Naming no names, is it?

Elisabeth   No.

Chief Inspector   And why not?

Elisabeth   Because of his position, I wouldn't want to do him any harm.

Chief Inspector   (*grinning*) Nice! Very nice . . . are you sure there aren't several fiancés who club together for this twenty marks?

Elisabeth   How dare you . . .

Chief Inspector   (*interrupting her*) Now, calm down, miss, I'm sure you'll excuse me if I'm out of order . . .

Suddenly he opens the wardrobe and is unsurprised to find a man in it, although the fact this man is a policeman in underpants, wearing only the jacket and cap of his uniform, seems to cause him some embarrassment.

Scene Eight

The **Policeman** *stands to attention in the wardrobe.*

Chief Inspector You?

Policeman Everything she said is true, sir.

Silence.

Chief Inspector (*to* **Elisabeth**) Would you leave us for a moment? . . .

Elisabeth *hesitates.*

Policeman (*to* **Elisabeth**) Please.

Elisabeth All right. (*She exits.*)

Scene Nine

Chief Inspector So this is where you spend your free time?

The **Policeman** *has climbed out of the wardrobe and is now hurriedly dressing.*

Policeman If you'd let me explain, sir . . . I'm sure there's been some mistake.

Chief Inspector Mistake? Where did you find this woman? We've got her under observation, we believe she belongs to a particular class of girl.

Policeman What class of girl?

Chief Inspector Use your imagination.

Silence. The **Policeman** *smiles.*

Policeman No, no, sir . . .

Chief Inspector How well d'you know her?

Policeman I know her.

Chief Inspector And you want to marry her?

Policeman I had it in mind, sir.

Chief Inspector How old are you?

Policeman Twenty-four. Sir.

Chief Inspector Same old story.

The **Policeman** *has finished dressing.*

Policeman But it's true what she says about the twenty marks, sir.

Chief Inspector Eighty marks a month! Are we overpaying you?

Policeman My parents help out.

Chief Inspector What's your father do?

Policeman   Master carpenter.

Chief Inspector   Perhaps you'd have done better to stick to woodwork.

Policeman   I'm not sure I follow, sir.

Silence.

Chief Inspector   I'm sorry about this, but you don't seem to be aware who it is you're proposing to lead to the altar . . . your fiancée has done fourteen days in gaol for fraud.

Policeman   Gaol?

Chief Inspector   For fraud. Not to mention a fine she'd already been landed with. For that kind of woman I can understand a relationship with the police might be highly desirable. But I can't think it'd be very beneficial to your career . . .

Policeman   I had no idea . . .

Chief Inspector   Well, then.

He opens the door and calls out.

Come in!

Scene Ten

Elisabeth *comes back in. She already knows it's over. Silence.*

Policeman   Fraud? Is that right?

Elisabeth   I know it's over.

Policeman   Gaol?

Elisabeth   Yes.

Silence.

Policeman   Listen, Elisabeth. Why didn't you tell me?

Elisabeth   Don't ask bloody silly questions.

Silence. The **Policeman** *stands to attention.*

Policeman   Thank you very much, sir!

Chief Inspector   Not at all.

The **Policeman** *clicks his heels and starts to leave.*

Elisabeth   Wait!

Silence.

Policeman   You lied to me, that's the main thing.

Elisabeth   No, your career, that's the main thing for you.

Policeman   It's not! But duty comes first and that's the way it will always be. Always!

Silence.

Elisabeth   Oh, Alfons. Just now . . . when you were in the wardrobe I tried to protect you.

Policeman   Me?

Elisabeth   Us.

Policeman   Yourself! Yourself at my expense! I know what's what!

Silence. **Elisabeth** *grins.*

Elisabeth   I didn't want to lose you, love . . .

The **Policeman** *clicks his heels again.*

Policeman   Sir! (*He exits, fast.*)

Scene Eleven

Chief Inspector   That really wasn't necessary, you know, to risk his career like that, most inconsiderate . . .

Elisabeth   Necessary? What about my career?

Chief Inspector   You're not going to pretend you were innocent?

Elisabeth   Oh, no, I gave that up a long time ago. I'm sorry, I can't help laughing . . .

She sits on the edge of the bed, silent laughter.

Chief Inspector   That's right, you have a good laugh.

He exits. Darkness.

Act Five

Scene One

Police station. After midnight.

The **Policeman** *(Alfons Klostermeyer) is playing chess with a colleague. It's raining outside and far in the distance (until Scene Three) a band is playing Chopin's much loved Funeral March.*

Scene Two

The **Policeman** *listens.*

Policeman   Who's that playing?

Second Policeman   The radio.

Policeman   After midnight?

Second Policeman   Maybe it's America. Still daytime there. It's your go.

Policeman   Right.

Pause. The **Policeman** *moves his rook. The* **Second Policeman** *ponders.*

Second Policeman   If I go here, you'll go there. If I go there, you'll go here. One fine day in the middle of the night, two dead men got up to fight . . . Bishop to C-3. Check.

Policeman   So that's the way of it. (*Pause.*) Whose go is it?

Second Policeman   Always the person who asks.

Pause. The **Policeman** *gets up.*

Policeman   I give up. Mate.

Second Policeman   Mate? With that board?

Policeman   I'm stymied.

Second Policeman   What about queen to D-7? Or knight to G-4?

Policeman   Suppose so.

Scene Three

The **Second Policeman** *is still looking at the chessboard.*

Second Policeman   Not like you to throw in the towel, you usually hang on to the bitter end, even when the prospects are hopeless.

Policeman   I'm not feeling well. For some time now. When I lie down I'm wide awake, when I get up I keep falling asleep.

Second Policeman   It's your nerves.

Policeman   (*smiles painfully*) Yes, well, I've just had a bit of a shake up.

Second Policeman   Professional?

Policeman   No. Private. Woman trouble. You put yourself on the line and do everything for someone, support her and devote your deepest feelings, your free time and your good money to her . . . and what happens? She makes a monkey out of you.

Second Policeman   Ingratitude how like a serpent's tooth.

Policeman   So sometimes I can't help brooding.

Second Policeman   You mustn't do that! Brooding's fatal!

Policeman   I don't care. Look . . . take my first fiancée, I got on really well with her, she went and died on me. So that's it. One dies, the other's a liar. Nothing but bleeding disappointments. I can't find anyone whose love's got something in it for me.

Scene Four

And now a **Third Policeman** *comes into the station bringing with him the* **Dissector**, *who's completely drunk . . . the* **Assistant Dissector** *is there as well, also a little the worse for wear from over-indulgence.*

Third Policeman   Right. Here we are.

Assistant Dissector   Now look here, officer . . .

Third Policeman   (*interrupting him*) Quiet! (*To his colleagues.*) Drunk and disorderly and disturbing the peace.

Assistant Dissector   How d'you get disturbing the peace?

Third Policeman   How do I get it? Wasn't he ranting and raving and banging his walking stick against the shutters, waking the whole street up? And did he call me a moron and a pinhead? Or didn't he?

Silence.

Assistant Dissector   I'm sorry, originally all we intended was a modest celebration of this gentleman's sixty-second birthday, but man proposes . . .

Second Policeman   (*grinning*) . . . and God disposes.

Dissector   (*shrilly*) And who's to blame? The Chief Dissector.

Third Policeman   Quiet! (*He points to the chessboard.*) Who won?

Second Policeman   Me.

Third Policeman   You? Beat him? Impossible.

Policeman   I'm not in the mood.

Dissector   Gentlemen! Who is my enemy? The Chief Dissector and only the Chief Dissector.

Third Policeman   Will you put a sock in it!

Second Policeman   Why's he keep going on about this Chief Dissector?

Assistant Dissector   Actually he is the Chief Dissector . . . I'm an Assistant Dissector and this gentleman here is my Chief. He was promoted last month, but when he's drunk, he always forgets about the promotion. The Chief Dissector the Chief Dissector here is talking about kicked the bucket some time ago, thank God . . . he got an infection off a corpse. From Brno.

Third Policeman   Will you shut up! Sit down! Give me the charge book!

Scene Five

The **Bookkeeper** *bursts in.*

Bookkeeper   Help, officer! There's a woman in the canal!

Policeman   In the canal?

Third Policeman   What woman?

Bookkeeper   A suicide! We pulled her out of the water . . . that's to say, not me, but this daring young lifesaver. I think she's still alive! Here they are!

Scene Six

Two men, one in a dinner-jacket, appear and with them the daring young lifesaver, **Joachim***. They're carrying* **Elisabeth***, who's been rescued from the canal. They lay her down on a bench.* **Joachim** *is completely soaked and frozen through . . . A* **Policeman** *hands him a blanket, which he wraps round himself. Everyone, except for the* **Dissector***, now busies himself with* **Elisabeth***. The* **Policeman***, Alfons Klostermeyer, also steps up to her, recognizes her and stares at her.*

Bookkeeper   There's still a spark of life in her . . .

Third Policeman   Artificial respiration right away!

Assistant Dissector   I know how to do that. May I be of assistance? I did two terms as a medical student but the money ran out and . . .

Second Policeman   Get on with it!

Dissector   And what about some schnapps?

Joachim   Yes, I'd like some too.

Dissector   (*to* **Joachim**) Real guts. Pitch-black night in November, jumping in the water . . . daring! Very daring!

Joachim   I was only doing my natural human duty. (*He drinks from the schnapps bottle.*)

Dissector   Too modest, you're too modest!

He takes the schnapps bottle from him and turns to the **Policeman**.

Isn't that right, general?

Policeman   I'm not a general.

Dissector   Well, here's to the daring young lifesaver! Cheers! (*He drinks.*)

Joachim   (*to the* **Policeman**) I was walking past and I heard this splash and then I saw a sort of silvery glow . . . that was her face. So I jumped straight in and grabbed her. Matter of honour. Anybody would have done it. You would.

Policeman   Of course.

Dissector   It'll look good in the papers. With a photograph. Long live the daring young lifesaver! Cheers!

He drinks again. The **Third Policeman** *is with* **Elisabeth**.

Third Policeman   Where's the schnapps?

Dissector   Here!

Joachim   (*to the* **Policeman**) Can I use the telephone?

Policeman   Over there.

The **Second Policeman** *comes up to the* **Policeman**.

Second Policeman   She had nothing on her. Except an out-of-date sales permit.

Dissector   Sales permit?

Second Policeman   That's right.

The **Dissector** *turns to* **Elisabeth** *and looks at her closely.*

Scene Seven

While everybody, except for the **Policeman** *and the two men, who have already left the police station, is busy with* **Elisabeth** *(administering artificial respiration and so on), including the* **Dissector**, **Joachim** *telephones his mum.*

Joachim   Hello, Mum! Is that you, Mum? . . . No, don't worry, I didn't mean to wake you up, but I've just saved someone's life, a girl who was trying to kill herself . . . Daring, eh? Well, it was a matter of honour. It'll be in the papers, with a photograph, how's that for a priceless ad for the firm, in all the papers for nothing . . . Hello! So do I get my motor-bike now? . . . What? But you promised! We'll see? Goodbye! (*He hangs up, furious. To himself.*) Silly old cow.

Scene Eight

Policeman   Is she dead?

Second Policeman   I think she's breathing.

Assistant Dissector   We'll see. We'll see.

Scene Nine

The **Dissector** *has recognized* **Elisabeth**.

Dissector   That's her. No question. The one who . . . (*He turns to the* **Policeman**, *repentant.*) Your honour . . .

Policeman   (*interrupting him*) Leave me alone!

Dissector   You must listen to me, please . . . I have a confession to make. That woman has been murdered.

Policeman   (*startled*) Murdered?

Dissector   I know the murderer.

Policeman   What are you talking about?

Silence.

Dissector   The whole business with the government inspector and the claims inspector . . . it was all my fault, m'lud! An eye for an eye, a tooth for a tooth! Take me away and get it over with! Do me a favour, hang me high!

Assistant Dissector   (*to the* **Policeman**) He gets pangs of conscience.

Policeman   (*to the* **Dissector**) You pig!

Dissector   Oh, God! (*He sits down in a corner.*) I'll be calm and collected on the scaffold . . . do your duty, hangman! And pray for me, good people, may you not be led into temptation, and before you do anything you might regret, remember me . . .

He buries his face in his hands and sits there shaking.

Scene Ten

Third Policeman   She's coming to!

Scene Eleven

Elisabeth *regains consciousness, but she's still not quite there . . . she sits up on the bench and looks around. She still doesn't grasp what's going on and remembers only gradually.*

Scene Twelve

Elisabeth   (*to the* **Bookkeeper**) Who are you?

Bookkeeper   Who, me?

Silence. The **Third Policeman** *passes her the schnapps bottle.*

Third Policeman   There you are, miss . . .

Elisabeth *is still staring at the* **Bookkeeper**.

Elisabeth   Who are you?

Assistant Dissector   (*to the* **Bookkeeper**) Go on, tell her!

Bookkeeper   Me? Nobody . . .

Elisabeth   (*smiling*) Nobody . . . (*Suddenly she looks around, frightened.*) Am I still alive?

Second Policeman   (*smiling*) Course you are.

The **Third Policeman** *is still holding out the schnapps bottle for her.*

Third Policeman   There you are, miss . . .

Elisabeth *is suddenly staring at the* **Second Policeman**, *terrified.*

Elisabeth   What's that you're wearing?

Second Policeman   (*somewhat confused*) What do you mean?

Elisabeth   Green and grey and silver . . . have you got me again? Now what have I done wrong?

Third Policeman   Just calm down. We're here to protect you. Don't worry.

Elisabeth   (*absently*) Who was it breathed on me?

Second Policeman   Just come back down to earth, miss . . . listen, you only live once, you don't want to go throwing yourself in the water.

Elisabeth   Was it you fished me out?

Joachim   Me.

Silence.

Elisabeth   Why couldn't you mind your own business?

Joachim   Oh, very nice.

Elisabeth   I'd got away and now it's all starting again, when no one's responsible for you and life is meaningless . . .

The **Assistant Dissector** *touches her shoulder.*

Assistant Dissector   You mustn't give up hope . . . everyone's life has a meaning, if not for them then for somebody else.

Elisabeth   Not mine.

Assistant Dissector   Yes!

Elisabeth   No!

Assistant Dissector   (*to the* **Second Policeman**) I can get really annoyed when I'm contradicted. I work with corpses on a daily basis and your thoughts automatically turn to the meaning of life. In my experience as an Assistant Dissector . . .

Elisabeth   (*interrupting him*) An Assistant Dissector? . . . (*Shrilly.*) How's the good old Dissector? Still feeding the pigeons?

Scene Thirteen

Dissector   Absolutely! (*He rises to his feet, full of dignity, if still a little unsteady.*) Those pigeons sit on my shoulder and eat out of my hand, my canary sings and I have a trained snake. I have a cage full of white mice and my three goldfish are called Anton, Josef and Herbert. I must demand, I must emphatically demand your attention. You don't seem to be aware who I am! I am the Chief Dissector, after all. And if I feel like killing someone that's a matter between me and my conscience. To sort out face to face with God! All right, officer! Good morning, all!

He exits. Everyone except **Elisabeth** *involuntarily clicks his heels.*

All   Good morning, sir!

Scene Fourteen

Elisabeth *catches sight of her* **Policeman**, *starts up and bites her hand.*

Assistant Dissector   Not now!

Silence.

Bookkeeper   I think she's hallucinating.

Joachim   It's no joke, you know, freezing-cold water this time of year on a pitch-black night.

Elisabeth *slowly covers her eyes with her hand, as if she were blinded by the sun.*

Elisabeth   Is that you, Alfons?

Silence.

Second Policeman   What's the matter, Klostermeyer? Do you know each other?

Elisabeth   Do we know each other? (*Silence.*) Go on, tell them if you know me . . .

Policeman   We know each other.

Elisabeth   (*grinning*) Good, very good . . . (*Silence.*) How's your career?

Third Policeman   (*to* **Alfons Klostermeyer**) What's all this about?

Policeman   Later.

Elisabeth   Why not now?

Silence. The **Policeman** *pulls on his white gloves.*

Policeman   I have to go. I'm on guard duty.

Elisabeth   Guard duty?

Policeman   In front of the palace. At dawn.

Elisabeth   It's still dark, Alfons.

Policeman   Everything's settled between us.

Elisabeth   You think so?

Policeman   It's over.

Silence.

Elisabeth   How simple you make it sound . . .

Policeman   Don't say any more, please.

Elisabeth   (*smiles maliciously*) Why not?

Silence.

Policeman   Don't try and start an argument for no reason. How can I help it if, if you want to throw yourself in the water? I stretched out my hand to you . . .

Elisabeth   (*interrupting him*) Pity you didn't cut it off!

Silence.

I'm going now . . . can you hear me, Alfons?

The **Third Policeman** *blocks her exit.*

Third Policeman   Stop!

Elisabeth *looks straight at him.*

Elisabeth   Good night.

Third Policeman   No.

Silence.

Elisabeth   Just let me go . . .

Third Policeman   Where?

Elisabeth   None of your business.

Third Policeman   Under the circumstances we're keeping you here. It's our duty.

Silence. Once again **Elisabeth** *smiles maliciously.*

Elisabeth   Are you taking me in again?

Second Policeman   Not into custody. Only into protective custody.

Elisabeth   Locking me up?

Third Policeman   In your own interests.

Elisabeth   Funny. Here you all are, standing around, stopping people getting their sales permits . . . (*She grins.*)

Assistant Dissector   Now, don't be childish . . .

Elisabeth   I'm not speaking personally, I don't give a damn about that any more . . . (*Suddenly she yells at* **Alfons**.) Stop staring at me like that! Get out of my sight or I'll pull my eyes out! And don't imagine I threw myself in because of you, you with the big future! I threw myself in the water because I had nothing to eat . . . if I'd had something to eat do you think I'd have even bothered to spit in your eye? Don't look at me like that! (*She throws the schnapps bottle at his eyes, but misses.*) There!

The **Second Policeman** *grabs hold of her arm.*

Second Policeman   Stop that!

Elisabeth   Let go!

Joachim   No, don't!

Elisabeth   (*yelling*) Let go! Let go!

Third Policeman   Quiet!

Joachim   Ow! She bit me!

Assistant Dissector   What's that? Biting are you . . . biting?

Elisabeth *cowers, intimidated.*

Bookkeeper   Biting the man who saved her life . . .

Elisabeth *snarls, baring her teeth.*

Scene Fifteen

A band marches by in the distance, playing the march 'Alte Kameraden.' Then the music fades and **Elisabeth** *sits slumped in a chair.*

Scene Sixteen

Policeman   Guard duty . . . (*He puts on his helmet.*) Mustn't be late.

Second Policeman   There's time, Klostermeyer. Wait for us . . . (*He pulls on his white gloves.*)

Third Policeman   We have to go too.

Assistant Dissector   What's that rumbling noise?

Bookkeeper   This lady's stomach.

Third Policeman   (*to the* **Second Policeman**) Have you got something?

Second Policeman   Sure . . .

He hands **Elisabeth** *a roll out of his coat pocket.* **Elisabeth** *takes it apathetically and gnaws at it. The* **Third Policeman** *pulls on his white gloves.*

Third Policeman   Nice?

Elisabeth *smiles apathetically . . . suddenly she drops the roll and collapses across the table.*

Assistant Dissector   Whoops!

Third Policeman   Now!

He and the **Assistant Dissector** *busy themselves with* **Elisabeth**.

Second Policeman   Just fainted.

Bookkeeper   Probably her stomach . . .

Assistant Dissector   A weak heart.

Bookkeeper   Stomach or heart, sheep or a lamb.

Joachim   It's no joke, you know, on a pitch-black night in November in freezing-cold water . . .

Assistant Dissector   (*to* **Elisabeth**) There we are, there we are . . .

Elisabeth *comes to and smiles weakly.*

Elisabeth   Can I see someone in authority?

Third Policeman   In authority?

Elisabeth   (*nods*) It's quite urgent . . . it'll be worse before it's better, but I never let it get me down . . .

She waves her hand in the air, as if she were trying to fend off flies.
Ah, it's these kind of black worms flying around . . .
She dies gently.

Scene Seventeen

The **Bookkeeper** *quietly approaches the dead* **Elisabeth** *and knocks on the table-top.*

Bookkeeper   (*cautiously*)Come in, miss. Your time is up!

Third Policeman   I fear the worst.

The **Policeman** *takes off his helmet. The* **Assistant Dissector** *bends over* **Elisabeth**.

Assistant Dissector   She's passed away. Heart most likely. We'll have a look tomorrow . . .

Joachim   All for nothing . . . (*He exits.*)

Scene Eighteen

Policeman   For nothing . . . (*He crosses to his dead* **Elisabeth** *and strokes her hair.*) Poor love. Just my luck. Just my luck.

Bookkeeper   I'm alive, but how long for?
I don't know when I'll die.
I don't know where I'm headed for.
I'm happy: wonder why? (*He exits.*)

Scene Nineteen

Assistant Dissector   A poet.

Third Policeman   Still raining.

Second Policeman   The parade'll be rained off.

Policeman   Probably.

Assistant Dissector   Well, I'll say goodbye . . . (*He exits.*)

Scene Twenty

And now a band marches by outside . . . once again playing the march 'Alte Kameraden.' The three policemen put their helmets on and leave the station, because, as you know, they're on guard duty. Only **Alfons Klostermeyer** *sneaks a last look at his dead fiancée,* **Elisabeth**.

An Illuminating Horror

Christopher Hampton interviewed by Jim Mulligan

Christopher Hampton had his first play produced while he was still an undergraduate studying languages at Oxford. It was partly a fluke in that he entered his play for a competition and came second. However, the organizers realized the winning play would be too expensive to put on so *When Did You Last See My Mother?* was staged instead, was well received and within a few months was produced at the Royal Court. It was the start of a productive career as a writer who usually works on a translation at the same time as writing his own plays and filmscripts. 'Most of my plays develop over a number of years. I keep notebooks – some of them for ten or fifteen years – and the ideas marinate in some way. Then when things coalesce, the writing can be very quick. I can write a play in a few weeks if it's all in place in my mind. I have made more than a dozen translations of plays over the years. It's a discipline like doing crosswords. It focuses the mind in a very minute way on theatrical language. I find translation work therapeutic and can turn to it when I am experiencing difficulty with my own work.'

After ten years of successful writing Christopher Hampton felt the need for the therapy of working on Horváth. 'For the first time I'd hit a brick wall. I was out of sympathy with what was going on around me and then I rediscovered Horváth. I first read *Faith, Hope and Charity* when it was published in a German anthology with one of my plays and it was so pertinent I couldn't believe it was written in 1933. This difficult patch with my own work persisted and I was able to deal with it by translating two of his plays. *Tales from the Vienna Woods* was one of the first productions in the Olivier Theatre in 1976, followed by *Don Juan Comes Back From The War* for the Cottesloe in 1979. During this time I was finding it difficult to address, in an appropriate way, the issues that were becoming apparent in our society but Horváth was helping. I finally got round to translating *Faith, Hope and Charity* in 1989.'

In *Faith, Hope and Charity* the difficulty for Christopher Hampton was to find an equivalent of Horváth's style which is very particular, elliptical, precise and rather mock-pompous. Horváth himself wrote: 'In my plays the characters are always trying to speak a little better than they know how to.' And his advice to directors was that the characters should never speak dialect but should speak like people who normally use dialect but are trying to use correct German.

For a time, Horváth became a central figure in Christopher Hampton's life, and he used the Hungarian dramatist as a character in his play *Tales From Hollywood*. Horváth had been killed in his mid-thirties when he was hit by a tree that had been struck by lightning on the Champs Elysées after he had been to see the film of *Snow White and the Seven Dwarfs*. In Christopher Hampton's play he imagines what Horváth's life would have been like if he had not died in this bizarre way but had gone, like other emigrés, to

Hollywood. 'As I read Horváth's work it became clear to me that he was the principal influence on all the young German writers for the theatre and cinema in the sixties and seventies. He wrote seventeen plays and two novels and it is said that there are no other books which give as accurate and telling an account of pre-war life in Nazi Germany. *Faith, Hope and Charity* was in rehearsal during the 1933 elections that brought the Nazis to power and they simply closed it down. It was never performed in Horváth's lifetime. In the play there is a real feeling of impending doom and of the political horrors that could easily grow out of the terribly ungenerous milieu in which the characters are living. It is very illuminating when you think it was written at that precise historical moment. He was attacked by critics for what they called his facile pessimism but he turned out to be bang on the nail.'

The play was written in response to a challenge to Horváth from a journalist friend who complained that writers were not interested in the small dramas that dominate the lives of ordinary people. He bet Horváth that he could not write a play about the real case of a young woman who had drowned herself because she could not find work. The result was *Faith, Hope and Charity*, a generous acknowledgement of Lukas Kristl as co-author, and the payment of 40% royalties to Kristl.

When he translated the play, Christopher Hampton thought it spoke of the way things were going in this country. He did not see our society on a slide to Fascism but there were parallels such as the inability of decent people to get work, the exploitation of women, the abuse of power, the contempt by those in authority for anyone below them and the powerlessness of ordinary people. In the play the characters such as the policeman and the woman in the corset shop are all people who have constructed their own universes and define them by the language they use. They rely on certain phrases and ways of thinking that they are very reluctant to see disturbed and, within this context, Horváth is able to probe beneath the surface. 'Horváth was the only writer of that period who could create a character like the Policeman. This man is terribly sympathetic and at the same time absolutely awful. He is so ungenerous and narrow-minded that he has no hesitation in betraying Elisabeth. He is basically a decent yet limited man but he is not patronized by the writer. He is just presented in a very truthful way. He would almost certainly become a Nazi because he is ultimately weak and because of his instinct to kowtow to authority. Although it must be said, there are people in the play who are more obviously Nazi material. It is a despairing play. It is very bleak. It is a hard play for people to accept today. They don't want to confront what they see all around. It is a strange paradox that, when things are really grim, people don't want to face up to them.'

Christopher Hampton's plays include: *When Did You Last See My Mother?*, 1966; *Total Eclipse*, 1968; *The Philanthropist*, 1970; *Savages*, 1973; *Treats*, 1976; *The Portage to San Cristobal of A.H.* (from the novel by George Steiner), 1982; *Tales from Hollywood*, 1982; *Les Liaisons Dangereuses* (from the novel by Laclos), 1985; *White Chameleon*, 1990; *Alice's Adventures Under Ground*, 1994.

T.V.: *Abel's Will*, 1977; *The History Man* (from the novel by Malcolm Bradbury), 1981; *The Price of Tea*, 1984; *Hotel Du Lac* (from the novel by Anita Brookner), 1986; *The Ginger Tree* (from the novel by Oswald Wynd), 1989.

Films: *A Doll's House*, 1973; *Tales From The Vienna Woods*, 1979; *The Honorary Consul*, 1983; *The Good Father*, 1986; *Wolf At The Door*, 1986; *Dangerous Liaisons*, 1988; *Mary Reilly*, 1995; *Carrington*, 1995 (also directed); *Total Eclipse*, 1995.

Musical: *Sunset Boulevard* (book and lyrics with Don Black), 1993.

Odön von Horváth was born in Austria in 1901 and killed in Paris in a freak accident in 1938. His other plays include *Italian Night, Kasimir and Karoline, The Divorce of Figaro* and *Day of Judgement*.

Faith, Hope and Charity

Production Notes

Setting and staging
This darkly ironic play is divided into short expressionistic scenes and is set in front of the Anatomical Institute (which the actors must be able to enter and come out of); in the office of Irene Prantl's shop; in front of the Social Security Office (which has a tiny garden); Elisabeth's bed-sitting room (with a wardrobe, bed and side table); and a police station after midnight.

Pigeons perch on the Dissector's shoulder and eat out of his hand. A decision will have to be made on whether to use live birds or take the safer option of using dummies with appropriate sounds to suggest contented pigeons.

The play contains clear and precise stage directions, and requires a number of **sound effects**: a fading funeral march; a band playing *Alte Kameraden*; the Radetzky March playing on the radio; and gunshots.

Lighting will need to suggest indoor and outdoor settings and various times of day. Side lighting will be needed in the scene outside the security office which is lit from the office window.

The play is based on an actual case heard in 1930s Munich. Set and costumes might be designed with this in mind.

Casting
There is a cast of eighteen, only four of whom are women. It isn't a naturalistic piece, and therefore some male parts might be played by women and vice versa. This is a play for an older age range, of sixteen upwards. A band is optional.

Questions
1. Among other things, the play is about the loss of civil rights and the inhuman application of minor regulations. Are these concerns as pertinent to society today?

2. Elisabeth's struggle is exacerbated by the fact that she is living in a male-dominated society. Where else in today's world might the play be given a contemporary setting?

3. Does Elisabeth's relatively lowly status allow her to be described as a tragic heroine?

4. Who is the most sympathetic/least sympathetic character in the play?

5. What lies are told and how do they affect the action of the play?

Exercises

1. Take Act IV, which is set in Elisabeth's bed-sitting room. Experiment with playing in two or more of the following styles: melodrama; opera; farce; *commedia dell'arte*; television sit-com; Brechtian. Decide which style is the most successful. Try applying it to other scenes in the play.

2. Find ways of moving quickly from one setting to the next. For example the band might be used to greater effect and become more closely involved in the action; some of the actors might, in character, move scenery. Avoid creating a hiatus between scenes by sustaining the momentum of the play.

3. Look at Elisabeth's speech in Act II Scene 5, which begins, 'I have a previous conviction because I once worked without a sales permit . . . ' Notice her frequent use of proverbs and clichés, in particular the phrase: 'but I never let it get me down', which she uses like a mantra. Compare Elisabeth's use of proverbs with that of other characters. Do they use them more casually? What might this tell us about them?

    Take this same speech and have Elisabeth deliver it as a soliloquy. It provides a very clear picture of her recent history. Apply the same treatment to some of the other characters – for instance, Alfons, the Baron, Joachim. Make sure all of the characters have a solid foundation of personal history to work from.

4. In pairs, explore a number of scenes which give insight into the relationships between the various characters. For instance, between Elisabeth and Alfons; between the Chief Dissector and the Baron; between the Magistrate's Wife and Prantl; between the Baron and Maria. Imagine the characters are animals, e.g. the Baron is a fox. See how playing them as animals affects their movement and speech.

Suzy Graham-Adriani
Director/Producer for BT National Connections

Stone Moon

Judith Johnson

Setting

Stone Moon is set in a village in the mountains. Although it is inspired by the granite quarrying villages of Southern China, it could be anywhere in the world and could be set at any time – past, present or future. Or a timeless place. On stage, we need to see or experience the atmosphere of: a village square with a well; a tea house; the porch of Kiri's family house, with the parlour in the background; the granite quarry; the moon.

Characters

Kiri A teenage girl
Asha Kiri's mum
Dena
Cossie } Kiri's workmates
Bess
Four 'Old Gossips'*
A Man
Kiri's Grandmother (a ghost)
Other 'ghosts of the well'
The parents of Shem (Kiri's intended)
Kiri's father
Women working in the quarries
Stone Carvers (men)
Waitresses at the tea house

NOTE: Because of the distinct separation of men from women in this society (and the effect that has on the characters in the play), it is likely that the male characters, especially if played by women, wear masks or use a similar device to enhance their 'otherness'

*Can be played by girls or boys

Scene One

The Tea House. Late at night.

A hen party is in progress. **Bess, Cossie, Dena, Kiri** *and other women sit around tables, dressed up to the nines, wearing ostentatious evidence of their well-earned money (lots of jewellery, rich looking cloth, etc). They are being waited on by waitresses who keep them topped up with rice wine. As we join them, the women are all drunk.* **Bess** *is beating on her table and they are following her beat, chanting.*

Everyone   (*except* **Kiri**) On the table! On the table! On the table! On the table!

They keep up the chant, getting louder and louder, until **Kiri** *is dragged/propelled to stand on top of the table. The chants die down.*

Kiri   Who's doing the honours then?

Bess   (*quick as a flash*) I will.

Kiri   Come on then.

Bess   Give us your hand then.

Kiri   No, you have to get up here with me.

Dena   (*to* **Kiri**) She's too drunk to stand!

Bess   (*threateningly to* **Dena**) I am not!

Dena *shrinks away from* **Bess**.

Kiri   Come on then, Bess. On the table!

She starts stamping her foot and chanting 'on the table'. The chant is immediately taken up again by all the women. This time **Kiri** *leads with the stamp of her foot.*

Everyone   ON THE TABLE! ON THE TABLE! ON THE TABLE!

The chant builds up once again until **Bess** *is propelled (with drunken difficulty) to stand next to* **Kiri** *on the table. The chant dies down.*

Bess   (*to* **Kiri**) Alright, alright! Give me your hand.

Kiri *gives* **Bess** *her hand.* **Bess** *holds it high in the air squeezing it.*

Kiri   Ow! You don't have to squeeze so hard.

Bess   I do solemnly swear.

Kiri   You're hurting me, Bess.

Bess   A serious business warrants a little pain.

Murmurs of agreement from the women, who have now become very solemn in their drunkenness.

Kiri   Any business warrants a little pain when you're involved.

Dena *laughs but no one else does.* **Bess** *silences her with a look and squeezes* **Kiri**'s *hand harder.*

Bess   (*insistent*) I do solemnly swear

Kiri   Ow! I do solemnly swear

Bess   That from the first night of my forthcoming marriage

Kiri   That from the first night of my forthcoming marriage

Bess   I will refuse

Kiri   I will refuse

Bess   I will wholeheartedly refuse

Kiri   I will wholeheartedly refuse . . . Tut! Get on with it.

Bess   (*squeezing again*) To let my intended

Kiri   Ow ow! To let my intended

Bess   My intended husband

Kiri   My intended husband

Bess   Lie down with me

Kiri   Lie down with me

Bess   For at least the first five years

Kiri   For at least the first five years

Bess   Of my marriage.

Kiri   Of my marriage.

Bess *lets go of* **Kiri**'s *hand (to* **Kiri**'s *relief) and smiles. She looks round the table at the assembled women, then begins another chant.*

Bess   What do we want?

Everyone   No babies!

Bess   What do we want?

Everyone   No babies!

Bess   What do we want?

Everyone   No babies! No babies now!

This chant continues and builds up, with **Bess** *and* **Kiri** *dancing around on the table top, getting more and more reckless until they are spinning around like whirling dervishes and they fall off the table. Everyone laughs their heads off. They sit down.* **Bess** *next to*

Cossie, Kiri *next to* **Dena**. *The party continues, though a little more low-key now. The other women chatter in the background while we focus on the main conversation. The waitresses continue to top up the rice wine.*

Dena Well done, Kiri.

Cossie I just hope she can stick to it.

Kiri Of course I can stick to it.

Cossie It's not as easy as you think.

Kiri Well, you should know Cossie.

Bess Don't speak to Cossie like that.

Kiri All I'm saying is, I have sworn not to lie down with my husband and I, for one, will stick to my Pledge.

Dena I'll drink to that! (*She raises her glass.*) To Cel . . .

Kiri There's no way he's going to get a baby out of me.

Dena Good girl. (*She raises her glass again.*) To Celib . . .

Kiri I'm not going to have his babies and live in his house and be his mother's slave. I'm an independent, wage-earning woman.

Dena Damn right, Kiri. (*She raised her glass again, but* **Kiri** *gets in before her.*) To . . .

Kiri To Celibacy!

Everyone To Celibacy!

Kiri (*after draining her drink*) If I had my way, I would never even marry.

Cossie What?

Dena (*worried*) Oh no.

Cossie (*exchanging glances with* **Bess**) What was that, Kiri?

Kiri If I had my way, I wouldn't marry at all.

Bess Oh dear.

Cossie Tut tut.

Bess I wouldn't let your family hear that.

Cossie Or your intended's family either.

Bess Marriage is a sacred institution.

Kiri Oh yeah. How come you all hate it so much then?

Bess It's not the marriage I hate, it's my husband.

Cossie And mine.

Dena And mine!

Kiri (*mimicking*) And mine!

Bess   Take it from me, Kiri. If you play the game right, marriage'll be fine. You've made a good match in Shem. His family are very respectable. At the Pre-Wedding Festival tomorrow, your mother and father will be able to invite them into their home for all to see. You've been lucky, considering who your family are.

Kiri   Yes. Well, my parents are paying them enough for the privilege.

Cossie   Have you met up with Shem yet?

Kiri   Not since we were promised to each other, and we were children then. I don't even remember what he looks like. What's the point? I don't get to say no to him, do I?

Bess   What would she want to meet him for? They're all the same anyway.

Dena   Lazy!

Bess   Spoilt!

Dena   Babies!

Bess   Living off our hard labour. No, she'll see enough of him after they're married. On Festival Days, when she has to go to his house and spend the night fighting him off.

Pause. They all look fed up. **Dena** *tries to brighten them up.*

Dena   Still. Kiri *has* made a good match with Shem's family.

Bess   Yes. And she ought to be more grateful! As long as she can keep him at bay, she'll be fine. She can keep her job, keep her money, and her family can hold their heads high.

Dena   (*cutting in, brightly*) I have a new robe for the wedding.

Cossie   Me too! A silver and blue one. Cost me two weeks' wages.

Dena   Well, mine wasn't quite that much but . . .

Cossie   . . . That's because you don't keep winning the Bonus like me and Bess . . .

Dena   . . . but I have bought a new bangle. I've got seventeen now. (*She shows off her arms, which are laden with bangles and bracelets, as are many of the womens'.*)

Bess *and* **Cossie** *exchange an 'unimpressed' look.*

Kiri   How many bangles have you got, Bess?

Bess   (*we see that she has less than* **Dena**) I prefer to spend my money on my rings.

She flashes two hands full of garish, ugly rings.

Cossie   Gorgeous.

Kiri *and* **Dena** *roll their eyes at each other.*

Bess   (*to* **Kiri**) And I suppose you'll be decked out in liquid gold from head to toe for your big day?

Kiri   Well, I have my robe already, but I've got a week left before the wedding. If me and Dena get one of the Bonuses this week, then . . .

Bess   Small chance of you beating us to the Bonus. No-one has yet.

Kiri   (*serious*) There's a first for everything, Bess.

Bess   Is that a challenge?

Kiri   What d'you reckon?

Dena   (*attempting to break the needling going on between* **Kiri** *and* **Bess**) Erm. Time for a toast I think.

She stands.

Dena   Raise your glasses everyone!

They all stand and raise their glasses, except for **Bess**.

Dena   To Kiri, to Celibacy, and to Marriage.

Everyone   Kiri. Celibacy. Marriage.

The women knock their drinks back. A moment of stillness during which **Bess** *and* **Kiri** *stare daggers at each other, then a big cheer and the party breaks and all the women disperse, giggling and chatting as they go.*

Scene Two

The porch of **Kiri**'s *family house. Night time.*

Music and or voices. Melancholy, chiming. People are strolling in the area, in couples. Celebrating **Kiri**'s *pre-wedding festival. In the background (the parlour), we see* **Kiri**'s *parents taking tea with* **Shem**'s *parents. A formal, ritualistic, slow motion ceremony.* **Kiri** *comes out onto the porch and stares at the moon.*

Kiri   The moon is big in the sky tonight, big and cruel and cold. Pulling the tides of the earth back and forth, controlling the waters of the world. They say us humans are mostly made of water. They say that the moon pulls on our bodies, pulls us like a swing, then lets us go: reeling, swinging, back and forwards like the tides. I want that from the moon. I want its power to pull me forward, drag me out of myself, send me reeling. Out of control. I want it from the moon because I can't do it for myself. Even standing here, just standing here outside, is too much. Even thinking these thoughts by myself outside while they sit inside and wait is too big a movement for me. People everywhere, celebrating this meeting of two families, this happy event, and all I can feel is frustration. Even the moon looks back at me with disapproval on its face.

Kiri *stares bitterly back at the moon. Her mother,* **Asha**, *comes out.*

Asha   *(angry)* Kiri, Shem's parents are waiting.

Kiri   Yes. I know.

Asha   Then come inside. Come on!

Kiri *joins her mother and they both go into the parlour and fall in with the ritualistic movements of the tea ceremony.*

Scene Three

The Quarry. Morning.

Music, voices. The brash bang of clanging drums and people shouting in raucous voices. Women rush in from all sides, readying themselves for a day's work. They put on work clothes. Big bright hats to protect their heads from the sun, jackets with padding to protect their shoulders from the heavy weights they have to carry, big heavy work boots to protect their feet from sharp stones. They chatter and gossip and laugh.

Bess I thought I was never going to make it this morning. When the cock crowed, I was still stretched out like a dog in front of a fire. I had to run all the way – (*To* **Cossie**.) I don't want anyone getting a head start on us for the Bonus!

Dena Stretched out? But it was a Festival Night. Didn't you spend it with your husband?

Bess (*pleased with herself*) Oh don't worry, I sent him packing. D'you know, he tried to kiss me as soon as I came through his door! I wasn't having that – I clouted him across his cheeky face and sent him flying down the hall.

The women all laugh, approvingly.

Bess He went off to play poker with his friends and never came back. So I didn't have to stay awake all night after all. Though I have to say, that bed of his isn't very comfortable, or very clean come to that.

Dean Oh don't talk to me about that. I don't think my husband's changed his sheets since we married. Every time I go there they've got more . . . stains on them.

Everyone *Eeeeeeeyuk!*

Dena I don't know what he does in there.

Cossie You don't want to love. Believe me.

Asha *and* **Kiri** *come in, deep in secretive conversation,* **Asha** *talking a lot and* **Kiri** *sulking, refusing to reply.*

Bess Oh, here comes the Wedding Party!

Cossie Morning Kiri, Asha.

Asha (*glancing up*) Morning.

Kiri *says nothing. They start getting dressed for work.*

Cossie (*to* **Bess** *and* **Dena***, whispering*) Oh dear, it doesn't look good.

Bess Ask her how it went Dena, go on.

Dena   She might not want to say.

Bess   You're her best friend. Go on!

Cossie   I'll ask, shall I?

Bess   Alright then.

Cossie   (*sauntering over to* **Asha** *and* **Kiri**) Kiri?

Kiri   Yes.

Cossie   We're all dying to know, that is, I mean, we're all em . . . wondering! Yes, wondering. And also concerned to hear . . .

Bess   Get on with it.

Cossie   . . . concerned to hear how you got on with Shem's parents – at the Pre-Wedding Festival last night.

Kiri   Are you?

Cossie   Yes. We, em, are.

Kiri   (*sarcastic*) Oh. Well thanks for your concern.

She turns her back on **Cossie** *and puts on her work boots.* **Cossie** *exchanges glances with* **Asha**. **Asha** *shrugs her shoulders and sighs.* **Cosse** *goes back to her friends.*

Bess   She's a stuck-up cow.

Cossie   I was only asking. It's not as if it's a secret or anything.

Dena   Perhaps she's upset, maybe it didn't go too well.

Bess   She's always upset. She's such a drama queen. Come on Cossie, let's get some work done.

Bess *and* **Cossie** *stand either side of a hefty block of granite and ram their shoulders together for support. They put a pole over their joined shoulders. From the pole hangs a long loop of rope which they pull around the slab of rock. They lift the slab swiftly, then move with slow, excruciating steps out of the quarry where they unload their slabs.* **Asha** *has started to pile smaller slabs into a big basket.*

Dena   You ready, Kiri?

Kiri   Yeah.

Dena *and* **Kiri** *lift and carry a slab in the same way as* **Bess** *and* **Cossie**, *following them slowly out of the quarry. The other working women are doing likewise in pairs, with some also picking up smaller slabs and putting them into baskets like* **Asha**. *When the baskets are full, they put them on their heads and carry them off slowly. Out of the* *quarry, they empty their ropes and baskets and come back quickly to the quarry where they repeat the process again.*

Dena   *(after a moment)* You're very quiet.

Kiri   Yes.

Dena   Was it awful then?

Kiri   I don't want to talk about it Dena.

Dena   Oh, OK.

Pause.

Dena   I remember how it was for me. All those years of being engaged creep up on you, don't they? When I had my first meeting with my intended it all seemed like a game, we were both so young, it was so far away. But before I knew it the time had nearly come. And I was scared.

Kiri   It's never been a game to me.

Dena   Are Shem's parents horrible then?

Kiri   No. No. Not at all. They're nice. As far as you can tell with all that formality and . . . I just, oh I don't know Dena, I just feel like the world is so small. And now it's getting smaller and smaller. And I want to push back the mountains, I want to kick a hole in the sky and fly through it and never come back.

Pause. **Dena** *looks perturbed. She lowers her voice.*

Dena   Kiri, you shouldn't say things like that. You'll be alright. You just have to put up with things. We all have to be married.

Kiri   When we were little we used to talk about running away a lot.

Dena   *(whispering)* We never. Kiri! Stop it.

Kiri   We did. You used to tell me we'd never get married. We'd run away over the mountains with secret lovers.

Dena   Well, I was a child. I didn't know any better. There's no such thing as love.

Kiri   Cossie loves her husband.

Dena   She doesn't!

Kiri   She does. She nearly had his child and they've only been married two years.

Dena   It doesn't mean she loves him. She just dropped her guard one night. She drank too much rice wine at the Sun Festival.

Kiri   That's what she says.

Dena   She was very angry about it. Why d'you think she threw herself into her work so hard? She had no intention of having that child and she made sure that she lost it. She was lifting twice the weight of stone she normally lifts. I can't believe you're talking like this, Kiri.

Kiri   I think a child born from love is a gift to be cherished.

Dena   What?!! Kiri, what's brought all this on?

Kiri   When we were little, we used to say that over the mountains, women could choose their husbands and that they sometimes even lay down with them (*Lowering her voice.*) before marriage.

Dena   Nobody knows what goes on over the mountains. People make it up Kiri. We don't even know if there's anyone there. You have to grow up and face reality.

Kiri   Yeah. That's what I thought. But now that reality is staring me in the face I don't know if I can. Not now that I've . . .

Slight pause.

Dena   What Kiri?

Kiri   Oh nothing. You know, Dena, after Shem's parents came into our house last night I suddenly thought, 'I can't do this. I just can't do it.' I ran out during the Tea Ceremony. My mum was very angry with me.

Dena   Kiri! You're meant to treat his parents with respect. They haven't called the wedding off have they?

Kiri   No. They were fine. Very understanding, in fact.

Dena   Thank the Gods.

Kiri   But then I don't suppose they want to lose the money they're getting when they get me.

Kiri *looks miserable.*

Dena   Come on, cheer up. You're just having Wedding Nerves. Everyone gets them.

Kiri   I wish that's all it was. I wish it was that simple.

Dena   What?

Kiri   I . . . I . . . Oh nothing.

Dena   What Kiri? Have you got something to tell me?

Kiri   No. Nothing. Maybe you're right. Wedding Nerves. Come on, we'd better pull our weight.

Dena   That's more like it. I know you want that emerald necklace for your wedding. Let's beat Bess and Cossie to the Bonus, eh?

Kiri   Music to my ears! I'd love to see Bess's face if we actually did it!

They lift another stone and move off as fast as they can.

Scene Four

The Tea House. Early Evening.

A cacophony of chatter. The Tea House fills up with women from the quarry, stopping off for a natter on their way home from work. A waitress moves about the tables, gracefully pouring tea. Some of the women are playing cards. Enter the four old gossips, women of an older generation. They wear old-fashioned clothes and look very bad tempered. Unable to find an empty table, they decide to kick up a fuss.

Gossip 1   There's nowhere to sit.

Gossip 2   I don't believe it.

Gossip 3   Nowhere at all?

Gossip 1   No!

Gossip 4   Well, that's awful. Haven't we worked hard enough in our lives?

Gossip 2   Haven't we walked many miles?

Gossip 1   Haven't we bent our backs low enough?

Gossip 3   That we must stand up amongst these young people to drink our tea?

They wait for a reaction but none comes from the women around them who continue to play cards, chatter, and drink tea.

Gossip 4   (*trying again, louder*) Haven't we suffered to bring forth children?

Gossip 2   Haven't we cooked?

Gossip 1   And washed?

Gossip 3   And cleaned?

Gossip 4   That now we have no table at which to sit down and rest our weary bodies?

Still no reaction. **Gossip 3** *goes over to the front table and addresses the women there.*

Gossip 3   Oi, mush, move yourselves. There's old people here, needing chairs.

The young women move off. The gossips sit down. The waitress comes over and pours them tea. They settle.

Gossip 1   (*after a minute*) This Tea House isn't what it used to be.

Gossip 2   When we were young, a table was reserved for older ladies.

Gossip 3   When we were young, the tea tasted fine as fine can be.

Gossip 4   When we were young, we gave respect to older folks.

Gossip 1   When we were young.

Pause. They slurp their tea.

Gossip 3   The market was too crowded today.

Gossip 4   So many people, I was nearly knocked off my feet.

Gossip 1   That rascal the butcher, he tried to sell me rotten meat. I may be old, my eyesight may be failing, but there's nothing wrong with my nose. His sausage stunk to high heaven.

Gossip 2   Yes, but what about his meat?

They all cackle loudly, leering at each other, slapping their thighs, then stop and slurp their tea.

Gossip 3   When my husband was alive, he used to say a fine roasted leg of lamb was the greatest pleasure a man could have.

Gossip 1   When my husband was alive, he used to say a fine glass of hot rice wine was the greatest pleasure a man could have.

Gossip 2   When my husband was alive, he used to say the sweet taste of a smoking pipe was the greatest pleasure a man could have.

Gossip 4   When my husband dies, it'll be the greatest pleasure a woman could have. And I'll tell you that for nothing.

Pause. More tea slurping. Enter **Bess** *and* **Cossie**. *They sit and are served tea.*

Gossip 2   Oh-oh, here she comes.

Gossip 1   Terrible business.

Gossip 3   Oh yes. Terrible business.

Gossip 4   Terrible terrible. Awful. What was it she did again?

Gossip 2   (*theatrical whisper*) She lay down.

Gossip 4   Lay down?

Gossip 1   With her husband.

Gossip 4   Oh dear, how long did she last?

Gossip 3   They say, only two years.

Gossip 4   Only two. Tut tut. Baby?

Gossip 1   Miscarried.

Gossip 4   Best way. Which method?

Gossip 2   Hard work. Heavy stones.

Gossip 4   Good. There's a woman with her head screwed on.

Gossip 1, 3 and 2   Definitely.

They slurp their tea. The focus shifts to **Bess** *and* **Cossie**.

Cossie   Oh my poor legs, I feel like they're going to drop off.

Bess   Don't complain, we have to carry on working hard so we can keep our hundred percent record on The Bonus.

Cossie   True. But look at this bruise on my shin, where the slabs keep swinging against me. Every day I'm covered in cuts and grazes and bruises and I feel like my body's going to fall apart. Sometimes I wonder if it's worth it.

Bess   Of course it's worth it. We're young women with money of our own. And since they introduced the Bonus Scheme, me and you have got more money than anyone! Make the most of it while you can.

Cossie   Yeah, because as soon as that new Sun Temple's built the Bonus Scheme will go. They've only brought it in to speed us up, so it gets built in time for the next Sun Festival.

Bess   You know, sometimes I look at the buildings they've made from our stones and I feel so pleased and so proud. Those fine houses and temples and carvings and walls. If it wasn't for us, they wouldn't have any of it.

Enter **Kiri** *and* **Dena**.

Bess   Oh, look who's here. Miss Hoity Toity herself. Evening, Kiri. Care to join us?

Kiri   No.

Bess   Thought not. Aren't we good enough for you or is it sour grapes because we won the Bonus again today.

Kiri   Nothing to do with the Bonus, Bess. You're just not good enough for me.

Bess   (*standing up, threatening*) Are you asking to get your head kicked in or are you just stupid?

Dena   (*scared*) She's stupid, aren't you Kiri? *Aren't you?*

Kiri   Yeah, Dena. If you like.

Kiri *and* **Dena** *go to sit at another table.* **Bess** *sits down. We focus on* **Kiri** *and* **Dena**.

Dena   (*cross*) You *are* stupid.

Kiri   I'm not. I'm just not scared of her, that's all.

Dena   Yes, well I am. So if you're gonna stand up to her do it when I'm not with you. OK?

Kiri   If more people stood up to her she wouldn't be so scary. The only reason they keep getting the Bonus is because she knocks into people and makes them drop their granite. Slows them down. If she tries that with you and me, she's in trouble.

Dena   Oh shut up. Why d'you always have to be so brave? It's exhausting.

Kiri   I'm not half as brave as I want to be.

The waitress serves them tea.

Dena   So. Are you feeling any better?

Kiri   I'm fine. I guess I was just a bit over-tired after last night.

Dena   I thought you were going to pass out!

Kiri   Me too.

Dena   Listen, shall I come round and see you tonight.

Kiri   I don't think so. My mum and dad will want to talk to me about, you know, Shem's parents, last night and so on. Me running out.

Dena   It means a lot to your mum, this wedding.

Kiri   Don't I know it.

Dena   Well, shall I come over later then. After you've spoken to them.

Kiri   Better not, eh, Dena? In case there's a bad atmosphere. Maybe I'll come over to yours later, instead.

Dena   Oh. OK then. What time?

Kiri   I'm not sure. I'll see how I feel, eh?

Dena   Oh. Right. OK.

Pause.

Dena   Kiri?

Kiri   Mm.

Dena   If something had happened to you that you couldn't tell anyone about, something that was making you unhappy – you know you could confide in me don't you?

Kiri   (*slight pause*) Yes. Yes Dena. I do.

Dena   OK. As long as you know. Best friends for ever. Remember?

Kiri   Yeah. I know. Best friends.

Kiri *drains her tea cup.*

Kiri   I'd better go home, face the music. I've been avoiding my mum all day.

She goes to leave.

Dena   See you later then.

Kiri   (*lost in thoughts*) Eh? Oh yeah! See you later. Bye.

*She leaves. We focus on the four gossips. They watch **Kiri** leaving.*

Gossip 1   *She* has the look of her grandmother about her. And something of her feisty character.

Gossip 2   Much more so than her mother ever did.

Gossip 3   Ah, but her mother has such a shadow hanging over her.

Gossip 2   Terrible business.

Gossip 3   Terrible business.

Gossip 4   Awful.

They slurp again. The chatter in the Tea House dies down gradually and the women disperse. Night falls.

Scene Five

The Well in the village square.

All is quiet. After a while, **Kiri** *creeps across the square and stands by the Well, waiting. Nothing happens for a while, then she hears a noise, jumps.*

Kiri (*whispers*) Is that you?

No answer. She sits down on the edge of the Well. An echoey noise comes from in it and **Kiri** *jumps. She looks into the Well.*

Kiri Hello?

Her voice echoes in the Well. **Kiri** *enjoys the effect. She does it again.*

Kiri Hello.

More echoes. Satisfied, **Kiri** *turns away from the Well and sits on its wall to wait. After a moment, another voice comes out of the Well.*

Ghost (*a sad, plaintive moan*) Aaaahh.

Kiri *jumps a mile and scutters across the square.*

Kiri What the . . .

Ghost Aaaah.

Kiri Is there someone there?

Ghost Aaaah, my heart, my heart, my breaking heart.

The ghost of **Kiri**'s *grandmother steps out of the Well. She is young, like* **Kiri**, *and soaked to the skin. She is sobbing quietly to herself. She balances on the wall of the Well for a moment, then begins to walk round and round it, looking down into the water.* **Kiri** *watches, terrorstruck.*

Ghost Give me the courage, oh give me the courage, oh give me the courage to do what I must.

The **Ghost** *repeats the above a few times, all the while pacing round the wall of the Well. Her voice is echoed by other ghosts of the Well. Suddenly, she stops and stands very still, then she puts her foot forward, meaning to step into the Well.*

Kiri (*running towards her*) No, no, no!

The **Ghost** *drops into the Well. We hear a splash and a struggle then silence.* **Kiri** *stares at the Well for a horrified second then runs like mad out of the square. A man steps out of the shadows at the side of the square.*

Man Kiri? Kiri? Kiri?

No answer, the man leaves.

Scene Six

The quarry.

The next morning. We are at the quarry top, where the men sit to carve stone. The men work in unison, lifting their chisels high, bringing them down to strike the stones they carve, tapping the chisels with their hammers, spinning the stones round to work on different sides. The sounds they make and the unity of their movements make a beautiful dance. **Kiri** *stands watching them.* **Cossie** *joins her.* **Kiri** *doesn't see her.*

Cossie   What are you doing? You'll be late for work.

Kiri *jumps.*

Kiri   I . . . I was watching them.

Cossie   Whatever for?

Kiri   I don't know. They look like dancers. Beautiful.

Cossie   (*embarrassed*) Don't be silly. They're men.

Kiri   (*also embarrassed*) Yes. Sorry! Your husband is a Stone Carver, isn't he?

Cossie   Yes.

Kiri   Can you see him from here?

Cossie   (*glancing at the men*) Yes, I can but . . .

Kiri   Don't you like to watch him sometimes?

Cossie   No, I do not! Kiri!

Kiri   (*sly*) Not even after the Sun Festival, Cossie? Not even now that you know him so well?

Cossie   (*angry, embarrassed*) I don't remember the night of the Sun Festival. I'd drunk too much rice wine.

Kiri   I'm sorry. It's just. You're the only one who doesn't complain about her husband all the time. I thought maybe you . . . Oh I don't know. Forget it. I didn't mean to embarrass you.

Cossie   You know Kiri, take some advice from me, it doesn't really do to ask too many questions.

Pause. **Cossie** *goes ahead.*

Kiri   (*following*) I suppose you're off to tell Bess that you caught me staring at the Stone Carvers now, aren't you?

Cossie   I don't tell her everything. You're lucky it was me that caught you.

Kiri   I'm not afraid of Bess.

Cossie   You should be, she's got it in for you.

They move down into the quarry, leaving the stone carvers behind (or the stone carvers disperse). The other women all start arriving, with the brash shouting and bang of drums we heard in scene two. Everyone sets to work. **Cossie** *is joined by* **Bess** *and they start lifting and carrying stone.* **Kiri** *is joined by* **Dena.** *They do likewise.*

Dena   I'm very cross with you.

Kiri   What? Why?

Dena   You said you'd come round to my house last night and you never did.

Kiri   Oh Dena, I'm sorry. I completely forgot.

Dena   Oh thanks!

Kiri   No, listen, something really weird happened to me last night.

Dena   Weird?

Kiri   Yes, I don't know if I should tell you about it, you probably won't believe me.

Dean   Why? What happened?

Kiri   I . . . I was in the Square, by the Well and . . . Oh no, I can't say, you'll think I've gone mad.

Dena   Kiri!

Kiri   It's just that I saw something.

Dena   Saw what, what did you see, what did you see?!

Kiri   (*lowering her voice*) I saw my grandmother.

Dena   (*slight pause*) Your grandmother?

Kiri   Yes. She came up out of the Well.

Dena   She never?

Kiri   She did, she did. And then she threw herself in again. Like in real life. It was horrible.

Horrified pause.

Dena   Oh dear.

Kiri   You do believe me, Dena?

Dena   Yes. Yes. But . . . this isn't good, Kiri. This is a Bad Omen.

Kiri   You think so?

Dena   Oh yes. Tell me, did she look at you?

Kiri   I don't think so, no . . .

Dena   Well, that's something anyway. It's direct communication that's the most worrying. Perhaps you just conjured her up by accident.

Kiri   Do you think so?

Dena   Maybe. You didn't call into the Well, did you?

Kiri   (*ashamed*) Yes, I did actually, but . . .

Dena   Kiri! I don't believe you sometimes. You know that calling into the Well brings forth ghosts.

Kiri   Yes, but I thought it was just an old wives' tale.

Dena   Well, now you know it's not. Are you sure it was your grandmother? It could've been anyone. Lots of women have died in that Well. It's full of ghosts. Most of them pregnant.

Kiri   Dena. If you became pregnant too early, and you couldn't . . . dislodge the baby. Would you throw yourself in the Well?

Dena   I . . . I don't know. Would you?

Kiri   Well. It does run in the family.

Dena   Your grandmother had already had her baby.

Kiri   Yes. At least she tried to carry on living.

Dena   Not for long.

Kiri   Yes. But she *did* try. She *was* brave. For a while at least. But nobody could bear that disgrace for long.

Pause.

Dena   Are you sure this was your grandmother's ghost?

Kiri   I don't know. It just felt like it was her.

Dena   Perhaps this isn't an Omen after all. Firstly, she didn't address you directly; secondly, you can't be sure it was her; and thirdly you called whoever it was forth – it's not as if it was them trying to get through to you.

Kiri   That's a relief.

Dena   Let that be a lesson to you, take heed of old wives' tales.

They work for a moment, then:

Dena   Just a minute, Kiri.

Kiri   Mm?

Dena   What were you doing in the Square? Nobody goes there at night.

Kiri   Oh. I was . . . on my way to your house.

Dena   But we don't live anywhere near the Square.

Kiri   Yes, but I was having a bit of a stroll around on my way to yours. Get some fresh air.

Dena   (*doubtfully*) Really?

*They pass **Cossie** and **Bess**, coming in the opposite direction. **Bess** deliberately knocks into them, causing them to drop their slab of granite.*

Kiri   Ay, what d'you think you're doing!

Bess   Ooh, whoops, sorry!

Kiri   You did that on purpose.

Bess   Are you accusing me of something?

Kiri   Yes, I am.

Dena   Kiri.

Kiri   No, Dena. I've had enough of her and her tricks.

Bess   Tricks?

Kiri   Yeah. Tricks. Knocking into people, making them drop their stones, slowing them down so that you and Cossie get the Bonus every day.

Bess   We get the Bonus every day because we're the best team. The strongest.

Kiri   Rubbish. I can lift as much as you can any day.

Bess   Ha! Alright then. Prove it. Lift that stone. Not with Dena helping you. Not with a rope. With your bare hands. Lift it over your head.

Kiri   You lift it.

*Pause. **Bess** stares around her. By now, a crowd of women have gathered round.*

Bess   Alright then. I will.

*A hum of excitement. **Bess** crouches down to the granite slab dropped by **Dena** and **Kiri**. It is very heavy. She strains hard but the stone doesn't budge. Encouraged by the crowd she strains again, over and over, until she slowly and painstakingly lifts it high above her head, like a weight lifter. The crowd goes wild. **Bess** holds the slab aloft for a moment, victorious, then slams it down to the ground.*

Bess   (*to **Kiri***) Alright, clever-clogs. Your go.

Kiri   Over my head, you say?

Bess   Yes.

Kiri   OK.

Kiri *crouches down to the rock. A hush of excitement comes over the crowd again, but instead of lifting up the stone,* **Kiri** *puts her hands and head on it and does a head stand. Amazement and anticipation from the crowd.*

Kiri   There, over my head. OK?

Bess   That's not over your head.

Kiri   It is from where I'm standing.

The women all laugh, uproariously. 'Nice one, **Kiri**', *etc.* **Bess** *is really annoyed.*

Bess   *(trying to get an acknowledgement of her victory)* No, no. That doesn't count, that *wasn't* over her head.

Kiri   *(getting up)* No. But it was a bit above yours, wasn't it? Hope that's tired you out nicely for the rest of the day. Come on Dena. I reckon the Bonus is ours now. Bess looks exhausted to me.

She starts a chant.

Bonus! Bonus! Bonus! Bonus!

The other women join in and the crowd starts to disperse, still chanting, laughing, patting **Kiri** *on the back, sneering at* **Bess**.

Bess   *(flustered)* But, I won, I . . .

Cossie   Come on, Bess. It doesn't matter.

Bess   Oh she thinks she's so smart. She thinks she can outwit me. I'll get her back. Miss Hoity Toity. I'll get her back for this.

End of scene. The women all disperse.

Scene Seven

The porch of **Kiri**'s *family house. Nighttime.*

Kiri *stands outside again, staring at the moon. Inside, we see her mother and father, sitting talking, looking at* **Kiri** *outside, worried. After a while,* **Asha** *comes out.*

Asha   Any better?

Kiri   Yes, I'm sorry. I think I must be working too hard. It's this Bonus Scheme, it's got us all working like madwomen. And only one team a day benefits. It's ridiculous, it's caused so many arguments. We used to all get along so much better.

Asha   Well at least today it was you who benefited.

Kiri   Yeah. Bess was livid. It was great!

Asha   I hope you don't faint during the wedding ceremony!

Kiri   Oh thank you. All you care about is that wedding.

Asha   It's very important to me, Kiri. My own wedding was such a . . . hush-hush affair. Your father has been very good to me, I was lucky he married me at all considering . . . who I was. Shem's family, they're so respectable, I feel like I'm stepping out into the light.

Kiri   Shem is just a Stone Carver, it's not as though his family own any land or anything.

Asha   But they're respectable, that's the main thing. You're lucky. Shem is young, attractive. I had to wait for an old widower like your father, no one else was interested in me.

Kiri   But you've come to love my father. Haven't you?

Asha   Love? Kiri! What nonsense. What *is* wrong with you?

Kiri   I. I don't know, it's . . . Oh mum. I just don't feel like I fit in to any of this. I feel like I've been born into the wrong world. Everyone says there's no such thing as love and that I am lucky to be marrying into Shem's family and how happy I should be but I don't feel happy. I feel like everything's wrong.

Pause.

Asha   Listen to me, my girl. I don't know what's got into you but you're going to have to stop thinking like this. If you carry on in this way you'll *never* be happy with your life. I blame myself. You've never had to struggle for anything because I've done all the struggling for you. You don't know how lucky you are. Can't you be happy and pleased and grateful for what I've given you? Can't you at least be happy for me. This wedding will be the best day of my life. I'll be able to hold my head up high and look people in the eye and feel proud. You don't know what it means to me to feel proud for once in my life.

Kiri (*quietly*) It's not my fault that my grandmother was raped.

Silence. **Asha** *stares at* **Kiri** *for a moment.*

Asha Who told you that word?

Kiri That's what people say happened.

Asha Yes. That's what they were told at the time.

Pause.

You shouldn't know words like that. *I'*m meant to tell you about those things on your wedding day.

Kiri What happened, mum?

Asha I don't know.

Pause.

When I was growing up my grandmother, your great grandmother, would tell me nothing. But on *my* wedding day she drank too much rice wine, and she told me that her daughter, my mother . . . lay down with a man . . . because she wanted to . . . not because she was forced to. My own mother. I was so ashamed.

Kiri But she wasn't married.

Asha That's right.

Pause. **Kiri** *looks scared.*

Kiri I didn't know that a woman could have a baby from lying with someone she wasn't married to. I thought it was this thing . . . this rape thing that made women have babies outside of marriage. Isn't that what rape means?

Asha It means that a man forces you to lie with him. A baby can come either way.

Kiri I . . . I didn't know.

Asha You have no need to know. No one I know has lain willingly with a man without being married to them. Except your grandmother.

Kiri She wasn't . . . raped, then?

Asha I think that's the story her family told. It was a lesser shame.

Pause.

Kiri (*angry*) Which is worse, mum?

Asha What?

Kiri   Which is worse, to be a baby from rape or a baby from love?

Asha   Kiri. You can't possibly understand any of this.

Kiri   What happened to the man?

Asha   He was cast out.

Kiri   No wonder she wanted to die. She wasn't even allowed to tell the truth. She wasn't allowed her love.

Asha   Love?! She was just selfish. Selfish! She deprived me of a mother.

Kiri   She gave you a life! Why couldn't you be strong for her? For her memory? Why can't *you* hold your head up high? Why do I have to be the one to make up for all this?

Asha   You haven't got a clue what I went through. Everyone knew who I was, a daughter born out of wedlock. A freak. Sometimes I wish she'd taken me with her into the Well.

Kiri   It's not my fault!

Pause. They are both very angry.

Asha   (*bitterly*) You're just like her. You really don't care about anyone but yourself.

Asha *stares at* **Kiri** *for a moment, then goes back inside. We see her being comforted by her husband.* **Kiri** *stares after her for a moment, then runs off the porch, into the night.*

Scene Eight

The village square.

A little later. **Kiri** *creeps into the square, apprehensively. She keeps away from the Well.*

Kiri Hello?

Immediately, the man from the other night steps out of the shadows.

Man Kiri?

Kiri Yes!

They run to meet each other and embrace.

Man I waited for you last night but you didn't come.

Kiri I did come but . . . something happened, I . . .

Man You're crying. What's the matter?

Kiri I had a terrible argument with my mum. I was really horrible to her.

Man Come on, come and sit down and tell me about it.

He leads her to the Well.

Kiri Not there! We might . . . fall in.

She sits on the floor.

Man Oh, OK.

He joins her.

Man What was the argument about?

Kiri Guess.

Man The wedding?

Kiri Got it in one.

Man You know Kiri, you really mustn't worry about it. I promise you it will all turn out fine.

Kiri I thought I'd be able to go through with it but now it's so close, I don't know, I wish I could just call it all off.

Man You can't.

Kiri   If only I could marry you . . . but then what's the use? We'd have to pretend we didn't love each other. We wouldn't be able to live together unless I got pregnant and if I got pregnant so soon, everyone would scorn me.

Man   Kiri. Everything's going to be OK. I've got my plan.

Kiri   So you keep saying. I wish you'd tell me what it is.

Man   Be patient. All will become clear.

Kiri   I love you.

Man   Do you?

Kiri   Yes, from the first time we met. We should run away together over the mountains.

Man   What? Don't be silly. We won't need to.

Kiri   That's what my friend Dena used to say when we were little. That we would have secret lovers and run away over the mountains. I thought it sounded so lovely.

Man   You're such a dreamer.

Kiri   So are you. Otherwise you wouldn't meet me here, would you? You wouldn't be so mysterious. I wish you'd tell me your name.

Man   I will . . . when the time is right.

Kiri   I came to look for you this morning, amongst the Stone Carvers. I thought, if he is a Stone Carver I'll easily spot him, but they *all* looked beautiful. So graceful in their work. Not like us women, lugging those great heavy weights of stone.

Man   Ah, but women hold up half the sky, as the saying goes.

Kiri   No wonder we're so tired all the time.

Man   Not too tired to lie with me for a while?

Kiri   Em.

Man   Kiri.

Kiri   Perhaps we should just walk a while instead? And talk.

Man   Whatever you want Kiri. Whatever you want.

They kiss. He leads her off. As they leave, an echoey noise comes out of the Well.

Ghost   Aaaahh.

Man   What was that?

Kiri   Nothing. Nothing. Come on.

She hurries him away.

Scene Nine

The Tea House.

A chattering of women as before. The four gossips sit in prime position, watching the world go by.

Gossip 1   Men.

Gossip 2   Ah now. Men.

Gossip 3   Have they a purpose in this world?

Gossip 4   It's debatable.

Gossip 1   It is indeed.

Gossip 4   When I first set eyes on my husband I didn't like the look of him one bit.

Gossip 2   Ah, but you do get used to them after a while, don't you?

Gossip 4   No. I still don't like the look of him one bit.

Gossip 1   I used to cry and scream when I had to go to my husband's house on Festival Days.

Gossip 2   Me too. I wouldn't speak, eat or drink when I got there.

Gossip 3   Not that speaking, eating or drinking was on their minds anyway.

Enter **Kiri**. *She sits near the four gossips.*

Gossip 4   Luckily, my husband always gets very drunk at Festivals, so he didn't give me any problems in the . . . (*Whispers.*) bed department.

Gossip 1   You were lucky. I used to go to bed with all my clothes on and sit upright all night with my legs wrapped in a blanket to ward my husband off.

Gossip 3   I refused to get into bed. I used to sit on a chair by the window, with all my clothes on and an overcoat and a balaclava.

Gossip 2   I used to stand up all night, fully clothed, with my overcoat on and a balaclava – in the kitchen. There was no way he was going to get near me.

Gossip 1   No way. Not in the first five years.

Gossip 3   I lasted six.

Gossip 2   I lasted seven.

Gossip 4   I lasted fifteen, and there haven't been any repeats either!

Pause. They slurp their tea.

Gossip 1   With my first baby, I got sick every afternoon.

Gossip 3   Oh, me too. And every morning. And every night.

Gossip 2   I wasn't sick but I did get very dizzy.

Kiri's *head jerks up.*

Gossip 4   I fainted a few times. One time I even dropped my basket full of stones on top of me. Didn't dislodge that baby though.

Gossip 1   No.

Gossip 2   They're not easy to dislodge, but it can be done.

Kiri *stares at the gossips. She looks shocked. Enter* **Cossie**.

Gossip 3   *(whispering)* Oh. And here's someone who knows all about that.

Gossip 2   Fancy only lasting two years, eh?

Gossip 1   Terrible business.

Gossip 2   Terrible business.

Gossip 4   Awful.

We focus on **Kiri**'s *table.*

Kiri   Cossie!

Cossie   Oh. Hello. Bess not in here?

Kiri   No. You can sit with me if you like though.

Cossie   Er. OK. Just for a bit before she turns up.

Cossie *sits. Awkward pause.*

Kiri   Was Bess very cross then. About the other day?

Cossie   You made a show of her. *And* beat us to the Bonus. She's on the war path. Believe me.

Kiri   She shouldn't be such a bully.

Cossie   You shouldn't be such a smart alec.

Kiri   I don't know why you hang around with her.

Cossie   She's a very loyal friend. If you tried keeping on the right side of her you might find that out.

Kiri   How d'you mean loyal? What's loyal about her?

Cossie   She stuck by me at a difficult time. OK?

Kiri   Oh. Right. Yes. I see.

Pause.

Kiri   Cossie? Can I ask you something?

Cossie   What?

Kiri   (*lowering her voice*) You know during your . . . difficult time . . . did you get dizzy and faint?

Cossie   I don't want to talk about that, Kiri. It's in the past.

Kiri   I know, but can you just answer me? It's important.

Cossie   Important?

Kiri   Yes. A friend of mine needs to know. Please, Cossie.

Cossie   A friend?

Kiri   Yes.

Cossie   (*slight pause*) Alright. Yes, I did get dizzy and faint.

Kiri   You did. Oh. And . . . and . . . how could you be sure that, that you were (*Whisper.*) . . . pregnant.

Cossie   Oh Kiri, your mum will tell you all this on your wedding day.

Kiri   Please, Cossie. Please.

Cossie   (*whispering*) Alright, but I'm not telling you anything else. You don't get a monthly show. OK?

Kiri   Monthly show?

Cossie   You know!

Kiri   Ah! Ah. Right.

Pause. **Kiri** *thinks.*

(*Depressed.*) Right.

Cossie   Now. Never ask me about it again, OK?

Kiri   (*worried*) OK.

Bess *comes in.* **Cossie** *jumps up.*

Cossie   (*to* **Kiri**, *loud enough for* **Bess** *to hear*) So be warned. Don't you ever make a show of my friend like that again!

Kiri   Eh? (*Sees* **Bess**.) Oh! OK, Cossie. I promise I won't.

Cossie *goes to sit with* **Bess**. **Kiri** *gets up and leaves quickly. She looks very worried. We focus on* **Bess** *and* **Cossie**.

Bess   She's got her uppance coming, that girl.

Cossie   Listen, Bess. I've got a bit of gossip for you.

Bess   Oh yeah?

Cossie   You'll never guess.

Bess   Come on, spill the beans.

Cossie   We . . . ell.

Bess   Cossie!

Cossie   (*whispers*) I think Dena might be pregnant!

Bess   No! Seriously? But she's only been married a year!

Cossie   I know.

Bess   What makes you think that then?

Cossie   Just something Kiri said.

Bess   Well, well, well. We can certainly have some fun out of that, eh? Kiri's best friend. I can't wait to start dishing it out to her.

Cossie   Eh? Oh no, we mustn't . . . I mean. Maybe wait until we're sure, eh?

Bess   They didn't wait until they were sure to have a go at you, did they?

Cossie   I don't think Dena ever said anything.

Bess   Are you going soft on me, Cossie?

Cossie   No. No! I just think we should find out a bit more first. Before we really lay into her.

Bess   Oh I'll find out more, believe me. I'll find out everything.

We focus back on the gossips.

Gossip 1   In some ways we've been lucky.

Gossip 2   How?

Gossip 3   Yes, how? I carried four children for my husband. All that pain and tiredness, and he wasn't happy with me until the fourth one came along and it was a boy.

Gossip 4   Luckily, my only child was a son. Else I would've had to go through that bed nonsense all over again. Yuck!

She shudders.

Gossip 1   I mean lucky that we didn't end up like Kiri's grandmother.

Gossip 2   Ah yes.

Gossip 3   Yes.

Gossip 4   Yes indeed.

Gossip 1   He jumped on her. Pushed her to the floor. Wouldn't let her go.

Gossip 1   He had to leave the village.

Gossip 2   He was despised. Spat on in the street.

Gossip 3   And try as she might she couldn't dislodge that baby.

Gossip 4   Poor Asha.

Gossip 1   Lucky Asha! So many mothers with unborn babies.

Gossip 3   Unhappy souls echoing in that Well.

Gossip 4   But all her life she has felt the disgrace.

Gossip 2   All her life she has carried the shame.

Gossip 4   Terrible business.

Gossip 3   Yes. Terrible business.

Gossip 4   Awful.

Gossip 2   Awful.

Gossip 1   Awful.

The chatter in the Tea House dies down and the women disperse. Night falls.

Scene Ten

The village square.

Kiri, *pacing, waits for her boyfriend. After a moment, he turns up.*

Kiri (*throwing herself into his arms*) Oh, thank the gods. I thought you weren't going to come.

Man What's happened?

Kiri I have to tell you something.

Man What? Have you had another row with your mum?

Kiri No. No. It's worse than that. It's, it's, oh . . . I don't know what to say.

Man What? You're not ill, are you?

No answer. **Kiri** *walks away.*

Man Kiri?

Kiri (*with her back to him*) I . . . I think . . . I think I might be . . . I think I might be (*Whispers.*) pregnant.

Man What?

Kiri Pregnant.

Man Pregnant?

Kiri Yes.

Silence for a moment. The **Man** *is totally gobsmacked.*

Kiri (*turning back to him*) I've been fainting, you see . . . and dizzy . . . and that's what happened to Cossie. And something else too, I haven't . . . Something hasn't happened to me this month that always happens to women and I've heard that means I'm pregnant too and . . .

Man I don't understand. How can this have happened?

Kiri It's because we've been behaving like we were married.

Man Like we were married?

Kiri Yes. You know. (*Whispers again.*) Lying down together.

Man Oh. Oh.

Kiri I can't marry Shem now.

Man Can't marry him? Why not?

Kiri Because of the baby!

Man But can't you lose the baby? Isn't that what women normally do?

Kiri No! I don't want to. I . . .

Man   But if you keep it, you and Shem will be Shamed. Nobody has a baby in their first year of marriage. There won't be enough money, you'll have to stop work, Shem's parents wouldn't stand for that. The whole town would look down on you, on him, on the whole family. It would be terrible! A baby would be terrible, Kiri. It would spoil everything.

Kiri   But I don't want to marry Shem. This is your baby. We must run away together. Over the mountains.

Man   No, Kiri. We can't. We can't. I . . . Oh Kiri, I don't know what to do. My plan, it's all gone wrong now. Oh Kiri. Kiri.

He backs off.

Kiri   Where are you going?

Man   I'm sorry. I need to think.

He runs away.

Kiri   Come back! Come back!

Man   (*calling back*) Tomorrow.

He's gone. **Kiri** *stares after him in despair. A noise comes out of the Well.*

Ghost   Aaaahh.

Kiri *turns to the Well.*

Kiri   Oh no please. Not now.

But her grandmother's ghost drags herself out of the Well and stands on it's edge. This time, facing **Kiri***. She stares at her granddaughter with eyes full of sadness.* **Kiri** *stares back, transfixed.*

Ghost   (*after a moment, to* **Kiri**) Leave . . . This . . . Place. Set . . . Me . . . Free.

Other 'ghosts of the well' echo the words 'set me free'. **Kiri** *legs it from the square. The ghost steps back into the well, her cry echoing as she falls.*

Scene Eleven

The quarry.

Next morning. The clink of the Stone Carvers as they hammer and chisel. At the quarry top again, **Kiri** *watches the Stone Carvers at work.* **Dena** *joins her.*

Dena Hello, early bird. How you feeling? Big day tomorrow! Oh, Kiri! You look awful.

Kiri Do I?

Dena You look as though you've been crying all night.

Kiri Yes. That's because I have.

Dena What's happened?

Silence.

Dena Kiri. Tell me what's wrong.

Kiri I thought I could push back the mountains Dena, but it's all gone wrong.

Silence for a second.

Dena Listen. I know you don't want to be married. And to be honest I don't blame you . . . My husband, he isn't what I thought he'd be. I was prepared for marriage in many ways but that was because I thought I'd married someone respectable. I thought, I'll keep my distance for five years like we're supposd to, then I'll get to know him, have a child and, yes, I admit it, I thought that then maybe love would grow. Like with your mother and father. Like with Cossie and her husband. But he isn't respectable, Kiri. He isn't even decent. When I go there he . . . he bosses me around. He orders me about . . . and sometimes, if I don't do things right . . . if I don't do as he tells me . . . he . . . he . . . hits me.

Kiri What?

Dena Yes. I hope I never have a baby Kiri, I hope I never have a baby because then I'll have to live with him all the time. But . . . but the thing is, you're here, you see. And if there is such a thing as love, then I love you. So I've got you and I've got work and when you marry Shem, even if he turns out like my husband, at least we'll always have each other. Oh Kiri, I couldn't bear it if you ran away.

Kiri Dena, I'm pregnant.

Silence.

Dena What? Pregnant? But I don't understand.

Kiri   (*blurting*) I had a secret lover and I thought we were going to run away together. Over the mountains.

Dena   Oh Kiri. Kiri. How could you be so stupid?

Kiri   Stupid?

Dena   Yes. Stupid. You've ruined everything. And your poor mother. Oh, Kiri.

Kiri   (*very disappointed*) I thought you'd understand, Dena.

She runs away down to the quarry.

Dena   Kiri!

Cossie *and* **Bess** *come over the hill.*

Bess   Ah, good morning, Dena.

Dena   What? Oh. Good morning.

Bess   And how are we feeling today?

Dena   Feeling?

Bess   Yes. A little nauseous perhaps?

Dena   What?

Cossie   Bess. We'll be late.

Bess   Or perhaps just a little dizzy, eh, Dena?

Dena   I wish I knew what you were talking about.

Bess   I'm talking about morning sickness, Dena. I'm talking about someone lying down with their husband in their first year of marriage. I'm talking about you.

Dena   What?!

Cossie *hangs her head in shame.*

Bess   You disgust me. You just let him lie down with you like the spineless piece of nothing you are. I bet you let him get away with murder. At least your friend Kiri's got a bit of get up and go about her. I can't see your precious Kiri lying down with her husband so easily. I wonder what she thinks of you now, Dena. Dena. Dizzy Dena. Dizzy dizzy Dena.

Dena   But it's not me that's pregnant, it's . . .

Dena *claps her hands over her mouth.*

Bess
Cossie } What??!!

Dena   Nothing.

Bess *grabs hold of* **Dena**. *She takes a handful of her hair at the back and pulls her head back.*

Bess   What did you say, Dena?

Dena   It's . . . It's not me that's pregnant.

Bess   Then who is it?

She tugs hard at **Dena***'s hair.*

Bess   Who?

Dena   I'm not telling you.

Bess   Not telling me?

Dena   That's right.

Bess   Oh, right then. So we can go ahead assuming it's you then, can we? We can keep that rumour going instead? I wonder what Dena's husband will think when he hears his wife is pregnant, eh Cossie?

Dena   Bess, please. I can't tell you, I . . .

Bess   I wonder what Dena's family will say?

Dena   Please Bess. Cossie! Don't let her do this. Please.

Cossie *looks away.*

Bess   I tell you what. Seeing as you can't tell me. I'll guess. Now then, I wonder who it could be. I wonder who would confide such a thing to Dizzy Dena? Ah! I know. Is it Kiri, Dena?

No answer. **Bess** *tugs* **Dena***'s hair right down to the ground.*

Bess   Is it? Is it? *Is it?*

Dena   Yes! Yes. It is.

Bess *drops* **Dena** *to the floor.*

Bess   Thank you so much. You don't know just how happy it makes me to hear the good tidings. And on the eve of her wedding too! Come on, Cossie. We've got news to spread.

They hurry off, leaving **Dena** *sobbing on the floor.* **Cossie** *looking back, ashamed. A brief burst of music/sounds, loud brash, frightening. Then a whisper starts up, made up of the following words, recited by the cast.*

Everyone   Scandal. Shame. Disgrace. Smear. Slut. Stigma. Taboo.

The whisper starts quietly, then spreads like wildfire, building up until it fills the performance space. **Dena** *claps her hands over her hears, then runs off, in tears, distraught. The whispers stop, abruptly.*

Scene Twelve

The porch of **Kiri**'s *house.*

Night time. **Kiri** *stands alone on the porch, staring at the moon. Inside, we see* **Shem**'s *parents talking animatedly with* **Kiri**'s *parents.* **Asha** *remonstrates with them, but they shake their heads. The wedding is off. After a while, they leave.* **Asha** *and her husband sit for a while in silence, comforting each other. Then* **Asha** *comes out to the porch.* **Kiri** *turns to see who it is, then looks back at the moon.*

Kiri   (*after a bit*) Thank you so much for standing up for me.

Asha   You have no right to expect me to.

Kiri   Don't I have a daughter's right?

Asha   You have brought shame upon shame to this house.

Kiri   Aren't you supposed to stand by me, give me support, defend me against all things?

Asha   Aren't you supposed to treat me with respect, obey my wishes, bring me joy in my life?

Kiri   What about some joy in my life?

Asha   You've ruined any chance of that.

Kiri   You've never understood me.

Asha   How many times do you think I've wanted to break out, to rebel, to just be myself?

Kiri   Then why haven't you done it? Why haven't you?

Asha   Because there are other people to think of than myself. If you go ahead with this foolhardy plan to keep your baby, you may begin to understand that.

Asha *goes back inside.*

Kiri   (*to the moon*) Please, Moon. Please pull me. Pull me forwards, drag me out of myself, send me reeling out of control.

She stares at the moon. The moon stares back. Nothing happens. She sighs, steps down from the porch, out into the night.

Scene Thirteen

The village square.

The man, waiting alone. **Kiri** *arrives. He goes to embrace her, but she steps away from him.*

Man   I'm sorry. About last night. I shouldn't have run away like that.

Kiri   No.

Man   It was a terrible shock to me, Kiri. I . . .

Kiri   Yes. I'm sure it was.

Man   So. What are you going to do?

Kiri   I don't know. The wedding's off. Of course. So that's something to be pleased about. I suppose.

Man   Kiri. I've got something to tell you that I should've told you a long time a go.

Kiri   Oh yes?

Man   I've been so silly. I thought I was doing the right thing, but I just let things go too far. It was my plan you see.

Kiri   Yes?

Man   You see. I'm Shem. I was going to be your husband.

Silence.

Kiri   (*after a bit*) I see.

Man   I thought, you know, because you wouldn't meet me, I thought if I could get to talk to you without you realizing, without all that formal stuff and away from the eyes of our parents, then when you realized I was OK, then I'd tell you. And you'd be happy to marry me then.

Kiri   But if we'd married, we wouldn't have seen each other from one month to the next.

Man   But that's the way things are, Kiri. Marriage is the only choice. And you have to accept that. You would've got used to it after a while.

Pause. **Kiri** *stares at him for a moment, then:*

Kiri   I'd like you to go now please, Shem.

Man   What?

Kiri   Go. You're not the person I thought you were.

Man   But what are you going to do? It's my fault too, what's happened.

Kiri   No. No. It's all my fault. I've been stupid all along. I've been very, very stupid.

Man   But we need to talk.

Kiri   Please Shem. Go. I'll sort it out. OK?

Pause.

Man   OK. If that's what you want.

He goes to leave. Hesitates.

Are you going to tell? Who the father is, I mean?

Kiri   No. You don't need to worry. No one will ever know.

Shem *leaves. After a moment,* **Kiri** *turns towards the Well. She goes to it and calls into it.*

Kiri   Hello? Hello?

Kiri's *'hello' echoes, then another voice comes back.*

Ghost   Aaahhh. Assshhh my heart.

Kiri's *grandmother steps out of the Well.*

Kiri/Ghost   My heart. My breaking heart.

Kiri's *grandmother stands on the wall of the Well.* **Kiri** *takes her hand and steps up to join her.*

Kiri/Ghost   Give me the courage, oh give me the courage, oh give me the courage to do what I must.

They both step a foot forward to jump into the Well. Suddenly, someone steps out of the shadows. It's **Dena**. *She is carrying a big bag.*

Dena   Kiri, Kiri! What are you doing?

Kiri *and her grandmother stare down into the water, still poised to jump.*

Dena   Please, Kiri. Get down from there. Get down.

Kiri   What do you want Dena?

Dena   I'm sorry, Kiri. I'm so sorry. Bess made me tell her about you being pregnant. I wish I could've been braver.

Kiri   It doesn't matter now.

Dena   Get down from there. Please. You'll fall in.

Kiri   I want to fall in.

Dena   No! Kiri. You mustn't.

Kiri   There's nothing left for me to do.

Dena   There is, there is. That's why I'm here.

Kiri *turns to look at* **Dena**. *She sees the bag.*

Kiri   What do you mean?

Dena   Let's run away together, Kiri. Over the mountains. Let's do it.

Kiri   Are you serious?

Dena   Deadly serious. How about you? You've been threatening to do it for years. Are you brave enough? Do you really have the courage? Come on Kiri. I can't do it by myself. I need you.

Pause.

Kiri   I don't know I . . . What is there for us over the mountains? How do we know that it won't be the same as it is here? Never being able to follow our hearts, held down by rules we never made. I don't want more of that, Dena. I want to break free. What if it's just the same?

Dena   Let's find out, Kiri. If we don't go, we'll never know. No one will ever know.

Ghost   Set . . . Me . . . Free.

Dena   Kiri?

Ghost   Leave . . . This . . . Place.

Dena   Kiri?

Dena *and* **Kiri** *stare at each other. Then* **Dena** *stretches out her hand. After a moment,* **Kiri** *takes it.*

Kiri   (*breaking into a smile*) Yeah. Yeah. Let's find out.

She steps down from the Well and they run out of the square as fast as they can. Suggested music: The Cranberries' 'Dreams' begins to play. As it does so, **Kiri**'s *grandmother steps down from the Well. She holds her hand out to other 'ghosts of the Well'. They help each other to get out of the Well one by one. Then they all run as fast as they can, joyfully following* **Kiri** *and* **Dena**.

Scene Fourteen

The Tea House. Many years later.

Cranberries fades down and continues to play in the background. The usual cacophony of chatter, then two old gossips enter. It is **Bess** *and* **Cossie***, now old and dressed in the same clothes as the old gossips.*

Bess   There's nowhere to sit.

Cossie   I don't believe it.

Bess   Nowhere at all?

Cossie   No!

Bess   Well, that's awful. Haven't we worked hard enough in our lives?

Cossie   Haven't we walked many miles?

Bess   Haven't we bent our backs low enough?

Cossie   That we must stand up amongst these young people to drink our tea?

No reaction from the others, who continue to chat. **Bess** *goes over to a table.*

Bess   Oi, move it. The older generation has arrived.

The girls at the table move, reluctantly. **Bess** *and* **Cossie** *sit down, settle themselves.* **Bess** *gets out a pipe and lights it up.*

Bess   *(after a minute)* This Tea House isn't what it used to be.

Cossie   When we were young, a table was reserved for older ladies.

Bess   When we were young, the tea tasted fine as fine can be.

Cossie   When we were young, we gave respect to older folks.

Bess   When we were young.

Pause. A girl comes in. She sits alone and reads a book.

Bess   Oh, look, here we go.

Cossie   Another intellectual.

Bess   I don't understand all this book-reading. We never used to bother with it. We didn't have books. It's only since people started going over the mountain that we've had this nonsense.

Cossie   Dreamers, girls like her. What's the point in all that reading? Doesn't help you to lift stones, does it?

Bess   Doesn't give you muscles or stamina.

Cossie   No.

Bess   She's like that Kiri, remember her?

Cossie   Oh yes, always dreaming. And where did it get her? Disappeared in the middle of the night.

Bess   Jumped in the Well, I reckon. Like her grandmother before her. Like all people who don't fit in. In The Well with them, I say. And good riddance to bad rubbish.

Cossie   And that Dena, too. Vanished into thin air.

Bess   Followed her pal with a good splash, I reckon. She was always following her around like a little dog.

Cossie   Never a trace of them found. And some reckon they ran away, over the mountains.

Bess   And old wives' tale. Nobody left in those days. It wasn't like now. Oh no, she's in the Well. And her baby with her.

Pause. They ponder.

Cossie   I may go over the mountain soon, to visit my daughter and her husband.

Bess   Tut. When she left, you said you'd never go and visit her.

Cossie   Yes. I know. But times change don't they?

Bess   Only if you let them, Cossie. Only if you let them.

They slurp their tea. A man comes into the Tea House and sits with the girl reading the book. They embrace, then hold hands over the table. **Cossie** *and* **Bess** *stare at them in disgust.*

Bess   Yuck, get the sick bag. Kissing in public, I'll never get used ot it.

Cossie   Come on, Bess. Let's go to your house and play cards, eh?

Bess   Yeah. Let's. This place has really gone downhill. It hasn't been the same since they started having music.

They drain their tea cups noisily, get up and leave, muttering to themselves on the way out 'Terrible business. Terrible. Awful', and prodding people bad-temperedly if they get in the way. The people in the Tea House ignore them completely. The Cranberries fades up again, loud, and plays us out. The End.

Living without Love

Judith Johnson interviewed by Jim Mulligan

Judith Johnson came to drama through her comprehensive school in Ellesmere Port, which she left without going into the sixth form. This was followed by casual work and A Levels taken at Chester College. She then took a teacher training course at Goldsmiths' College in South London, and a creative and performing arts course at Newcastle Polytechnic. After Newcastle she was on the dole, and to fill her time, started writing plays. She submitted one to a women's writing competition, and her success here encouraged her to keep writing, meeting people in the theatre, and submitting scripts. It also led to a spell at the Liverpool Everyman, devising and scripting plays for young unemployed people, followed by a period with the Red Ladder company in Leeds. *Stone Moon* was commissioned by the Royal National Theatre while Judith Johnson was writer-in-residence at the National's Studio. 'I write for adult and youth theatre. In one way, youth theatre is restrictive because you have to write something that young people can handle and they don't have the budget and resources of the professional theatre. But they have different resources, personal experiences and imaginative energy. I write more realistically and personally for the adult theatre, but with youth theatre I can explore different worlds and different societies.'

The inspiration for *Stone Moon* came from an article in *Marie Claire*, read at the hairdressers, about women who work in the granite quarries in South China and the way their physically demanding work gives them a freedom that other women in rural China do not experience. They cling fiercely to this independence and devise all kinds of ways to avoid having children because, once that happens, they have to go to live with their husbands. 'It seemed amazing to me that there could be societies like that in the world today. I thought it would be interesting for young women to look at the relationships in the play which might be extreme versions of what is going on in their own lives, but far enough removed for them to look at things dispassionately.'

The hen party that starts the play was put in after the first draft to make clear some of the conventions of the society and also to show the women having a good time and displaying their finery and wealth. It shows their capacity to have fun despite the limits imposed upon them. 'That party is not a million miles away from some of the hen parties I've been to where women get drunk and dance on the tables. It's the Chippendale phenomenon: women go out for the night and exclude men so that they can have a good laugh.'

The women in *Stone Moon* are kept ignorant of sex and the tradition is that they are told at their wedding-feast what they must do and the conventions surrounding sex. There is no love in the society and this deprivation is deliberately created because if the women started to understand sexual love, their attitude to men might change and all the hidden feelings that they cannot understand and put a name to would surface. 'There would be more intermingling of the sexes, the economic basis of their society would be threatened and their status as women with wealth and independence would be undermined. These repressed societies are not that uncommon. When I was doing research for another work, I read about women of my mother's and grandmother's age. Some of the things they said could have come straight out of *Stone Moon*. One woman, for example, said that when she was 18 a man took her down a back alley and did something to her she didn't understand, and she later found she was pregnant. And that was only 50 years ago in England.'

Because of her nature it is important for Kiri to find her fulfilment in her society but, because she is a free spirit, she cannot reconcile herself to the way things are. She thinks she has found a way out by having a clandestine love affair with Shem, but when he cannot bring himself to leave the valley with her, she is lost. It is only when Dena, who has much less courage than Kiri, is forced by domestic violence to leave her husband, that both of them find the strength to make a move.

'In my play it comes as a great shock to the women to learn that Dena's husband has been hitting her, but none of the women know what is really going on. It might be that some women are having sex and really enjoying themselves or, as far as Dena knows, everyone might be getting a crack from their husbands.'

Judith Johnson deliberately does not reflect on the role of the men in the *Stone Moon* society, but it is obvious that their lives must have been as restricted as the women's. Nor does she look at the previous generations, but she gives a hint of what went on before by using the spirit world. To do this she focuses on the grandmother and confines the spirits to the well.

'The floodgates are opened when Kiri and Dena find the strength in their love and friendship to leave the valley. Then all the women from previous generations, who in their time were rebels, stream out and follow them up the hillside. Those were the women who had not the strength to leave when they were alive and who suffered dreadfully for their independence. But their spirits escape. And in the final scene we see that things are changing. There are negative things in the play. There is the bullying by Bess – but that is imposed upon her by a society where you have to be tough and hard and big and strong. And Kiri is horrible to her mother. Kiri understands how much the marriage means to her mother, who is also only acting in accordance with the rules of the society, yet Kiri speaks the things that should have been left unspoken and so destroys her mother. But overall the play is positive. Kiri does escape, the society is changing, and Bess is somewhat more mellow at the end. I suppose *Stone Moon* is saying that even in repressed societies it is possible to find some kind of contentment and that a free spirit will find a way out.'

Judith Johnson is from Liverpool, and has had many stage plays produced, including: *Working Away* (Soho Poly, 1989); *The Edge* and *Le Camp* (community plays which toured London's East End); *Death Party* devised for the Liverpool Everyman's 'Acting Up' course; *The Scrappie* for Red Ladder Theatre

Company, which did a national tour of youth clubs; and *Los Escombros*, commissioned by the National Theatre Education Department and performed by the National's Young People's Theatre Group in 1992. *Nowheresville* was shortlisted for the Verity Bargate Award and *Somewhere* was produced at the Liverpool Everyman and in the Cottesloe Theatre at the National in 1993. It is published by Methuen Drama in *Frontline Intelligence 1*. *Uganda* was produced at the Royal Court Theatre in association with the National's Studio in 1995, and is published by Methuen Drama in *Frontline Intelligence 3*.

Stone Moon

Production Notes

Setting and staging
The play is set in an unspecified country and time, in a remote village. On stage, the atmosphere of the following need to be created: a village square with a well; a tea-house; a granite quarry; the porch of Kiri's house; plus the moon (which could be an additional character).

There is emphasis on **sound and movement**, and not on lavish sets. Echoes and ghostly watery sounds issue from the well. The women chant with menace; they are frequently accompanied by the clanging of drums and loud, frightening sounds.

The atmosphere of the tea house can be created by the ritualistic movements of the tea ceremony. In contrast, the cast must create the atmosphere of the stone quarry by suggesting the hard labour of transporting granite slabs with the help of poles, or by balancing smaller pieces on their heads.

Male characters are separated in this society, and their 'otherness' might be emphasised by specific movement (perhaps delicate, perhaps sensitive?)

Costume
There is scope for creating curious personal decoration for the women, who are positive 'magpies' off duty. Their work clothes must be practical and padded, offering head and body protection from the heavy granite.

Lighting needs to take into account the passage of time, particularly day turning into night – shadows in the courtyard, sharply contrasting with the harsh light of the working day.

Casting
The play requires a cast of at least twenty: Kiri (who must be able to do a headstand). Her best friend, Dena. Her work mates, Bess and Cossie, who are probably of the same age. Asha, Kiri's mother. Four old gossips (who could be played by boys or girls, young or old). Kiri's grandmother/ghost. Shem (a young man). The other parts are non-speaking.

The play is appropriate for twelve-year-olds upwards, and has very accessible dialogue. It is perfectly possible to cast the play with an all-female company, in which case the male characters might be played in masks, or even represented in another symbolic form, such as puppets, or silhouettes, shadows, and/or offstage voices.

The characters all have lots of spirit, but they are governed by strong rules and traditions in their society.

Questions

1. How might the women reinforce their support for each other? For example, do they have songs they make up as a group? Do they have games they play together?

2. How is status decided within the group? How are key decisions arrived at?

3. What are the key characteristics of the women's relationships with men, either as employers or as domestic partners? How are these characteristics expressed in everyday life?

4. The play does not criticize the concept of arranged marriage, but it criticizes lack of love. How is this evident in the actions of the characters?

5. What similarities exist in today's Western society and the society in the play? Would it make dramatic sense to underline these similarities in the production?

6. Why is it necessary for the women to separate themselves from the men? How do they express this?

7. How do the taboos and peer-pressures in this society influence the decisions the characters must make?

8. Who occupy the well and what might they symbolize?

9. Where are Kiri and Dena running to at the end of the play, and from what are they hoping to escape? How does this affect their behaviour in the play?

10. Has the passage of time had any effect on the society at the end of the play?

Exercises

1. A pair take two chairs and place them opposite each other. One will argue for, the other against. The challenge is to believe the view being expressed on the following discussions: for and against love; for and against family; for and against sex. The exploration of these issues can result in a greater understanding of the text. Once the discussion becomes heated, the pair can swap places and reverse the argument.

2. Select a dialogue, from scene seven for instance. Run it and then 'hot-seat' Kiri and her mother. Establish what expectations mother and daughter have of one another. Improvise the scene, emphasising how each attempts to get her own way, and the differences in approach between the two women.

3. Create the men's world of work, by inventing the synchronized movements which accompany the cutting of the granite. Give the men

voices and improvise a scene which illustrates the male perspective of this society.

4.   Create a series of improvisations based on the questions in the preceding section.

Suzy Graham-Adriani,
Director/Producer for BT National Connections

The Forest of Mirrors

Gregory Motton

A man thumps his door, weeping 'Let me in'. A young woman stands around outside aimlessly. Two men stand watching.

First Man   Why is that man thumping at that door? Who lives there?

Second Man   He does, alone.

First Man   He's dogged by some sort of misconception, surely.

Second Man   Looks like it.

First Man   How does it normally resolve itself?

Second Man   He gives up.

First Man   And . . .?

The man lets himself in saying: 'It's no use.' Goes inside.

It's sad, he can never get satisfaction.

Second Man   Not in this life anyway, that's for certain.

First Man   So what about the story?

Second Man   Oh well, King Cnut is just about to get married, and well, you know what love is. The bride ran off and left him for this monster who lived on a rock in the sea surrounded by giant fish, but along comes Fitz the Faithful and another man quite like himself called Fitz the Unfaithful whom he'd met on the roadside and who helped him with a job out of the goodness of his heart, a job to go and fetch the missing bride.

First Man   What's the point of all that?

Second Man   The point is that it ends up with the king and the giant wandering about in the swamp talking to themselves out of sheer desperation, and in fact, they all end up in the swamp one way or another, but love conquers all.

First Man   And what's the moral of the story?

Second Man   Well . . . there is one. And if you can't see it . . . you're a bigger fool than I am for telling it.

First Man   But what is it?

Second Man   Alright I'll tell you. This is it.

In the Monster Ryan's Palace.

Girl   Who are you?

Fitz the Faithful   I'm Fitz the Faithful. I've come to take you back to your husband the king.

Girl   But I'm in the middle of loving this man.

Fitz the Faithful   Who is he, that wretch? What is he? Is he concerned for your welfare? He's a gargoyle. He kidnapped you, he's insulted your husband.

Girl   You don't know. He's good to me. See this bed I lie on, it's soft, it doesn't crick my neck. Please don't take me away, not now.

Fitz the Faithful   You can't be late for your wedding.

Girl   Just one more afternoon of love and sunshine.

Fitz the Faithful   You'll break his majesty's heart.

Girl   What do you know? Who are you? Was this his idea? I bet it wasn't.

Fitz the Faithful   No, it was my brother's idea, Fitz the Unfaithful.

Girl   Good of him. And where is he now to help you? Or did the fish eat him?

Fitz the Faithful   No, in fact I placated the fish with good advice. Why don't you wake your lover and ask him why his castle rock isn't better guarded? Perhaps he wanted to be found, wanted you to be taken off his hands.

Girl   I'm going to wake him. I wanted to talk to you first.

Fitz the Faithful   You'd better make up your mind to come with me.

Girl   And if I don't?

Fitz the Faithful   I'll sling you over my shoulder.

Girl   I'll scream. He'll wake up and kill you.

Fitz the Faithful   I'll reason with him.

Girl   I'd like to see you try. Ryan, Ryan! You see, he's stirring. You've had it now.

Fitz the Faithful   Wake up, Ryan you pig. I've breached your defences.

Ryan   Ha! my defences have been breached. They're always breached. That's not worth waking up for.

Fitz the Faithful   Then hear this, I'm taking her away back to the king.

Ryan   Back to the king, eh? And do you really think he wants her? Look at her, she's bed-soiled. She's dribbling, she has little fits and goes into a coma if I don't feed her right. She's treacherous. She'll betray him as she betrayed me as she betrayed him as she'll betray you.

Fitz the Faithful   She won't betray me, she loves me already.

Ryan   Show me a man she hasn't loved and I'll show you a man she hasn't betrayed.

Fitz the Faithful   That's enough. I'm taking her now.

Ryan   All right. Darling, you have touched my heart with your . . . I am ready to die for you if you require it, or to slay this gnat in his boots, just one word from you. But I know that word won't come. Remember the magic we shared together, those exquisite moments of fear. Light a candle for me in one of your churches, I'll throw rocks at the moon for you.

Girl   Ryan, if you knew to what fate I go now, you'd tear me in two with your bare arms and throw me into the lake.

Ryan *snores.*

Fitz the Faithful   You see, he's asleep. You'd better come with me.

Girl   What did the king say when he found me gone?

King Cnut's Castle.

Cnut   This was your idea, whoever you are. Why did you recommend this man to me?

Fitz the Unfaithful   Don't worry, I trust him better than I trust myself.

Cnut   Where are they? You said they'd been seen coming ashore.

Fitz the Unfaithful   Look at it this way. If he doesn't bring her back, it's likely she'll return of her own free will, some day.

Cnut   But then I'll be old.

Fitz the Unfaithful   Oh not so old. Her youth will be over sooner than yours.

Cnut   You are an imposter. You came up from the shadows and the only person who knows you is a barmaid.

Fitz the Unfaithful   Then that's two of us she knows. I arrived to help you in a moment of weakness. I'm like a brother to you. I have sacrificed my best friend in this world, my twin, just to help you. Where is he now do you think? Being strangled by some monstrous fish in those foul bubbling waters. All for what? He's a man worth ten. He eclipses me.

Cnut   Where did you meet this nincompoop?

Fitz the Unfaithful   On the roadside. I was just about to rob him when he took out his purse and offered me alms. He thought I was a beggar. Idiot. Is he blind? I vowed to get even. Robbery was too good for him, and frankly I was too embarrassed.

Cnut   So, you've deliberately delivered me into the hands of a fool!

Fitz the Unfaithful   Alright, yes. To get rid of him. Because I've got a better plan. Don't you think you should go and get your bride back yourself? Don't you know anything about women?

Cnut   And what if I'm humiliated by her in front of my enemy?

Fitz the Unfaithful   Of course! Think what a pungent sauce that will be to your new life together! She's offering you an adventure.

Cnut   I've had enough of you now. I command you to walk out of that door and not stop until you come to the beach. Then use your charm to push back the sea. Then keep walking, driving the waves before you. Good luck.

Fitz the Unfaithful   Alright. If that's how you feel. But don't think that if I'm waylaid by continuous strokes of good luck in the meantime that I'll be in any hurry to fulfil your orders, because do you know what, you're the kind of man who sends others to do what you'd like to be able to do yourself. (*Exits.*)

Cnut   Perhaps a small grain of truth. Anyone for a game of chess?

Voices Off   No thanks!!

The shore of the lake.

Girl   So you think this is a wild adventure, I bet you do. You suppose you have me now, rescued me from that horrible rock in the sea. Wasn't it ugly? Wasn't it grey and black and foul. It was as if the waves lashed it to punish it for its refusal to bear fruit. But it bore you me, didn't it?

Fitz the Faithful   I had a bargain with those waves and all the freaks and monsters there.

Girl   Oh? And what could you give them?

Fitz the Faithful   Those outcasts down there savour goodness like a certain kind of lover does fidelity; as an occasional sauce.

Girl   You're pleased now you're at the lip of the sea, I can tell, your white tunic doing its moonlight dance in the foam like a young girl's petticoat, but I've news for you Tam O'Shanter, you have to go back, I've forgotten my letters.

Fitz the Faithful   Letters, what letters?

Girl   What letters? Do you expect a girl to go about without letters? Don't you think I have friends, lovers, a husband? I'm in regular contact. Sometimes of course I write them up here in my head . . . if there is no paper and really nothing else to write on, like if I'm in the middle of the sea. But usually I find something. There I did. You'll find them on scraps of wallpaper, you'll have to peel them off carefully, on bits of table, the tops of shelves, the cat flap, the sole of his lordship's boot. There are a dozen in all. Don't think I'm coming back with you until I have the full whack.

He starts to go.

Girl Tell me, what is the king like?

Fitz the Faithful You must know. You were about to marry him.

Girl I fell in love to avoid being alone forever. But will he keep me good company, will he understand me, will he love me as a woman, will he save himself for me, will he keep his wisdom to himself, will he know to be humble in failure and no boaster in victory, will he count his victories over me as defeats?

In the water, two old fish.

First Fish What are you back for?

Fitz the Faithful She forgot her letters. I'm swimming back to the island to get them.

Second Fish You don't expect us to let you through so easily this time surely?

Fitz the Faithful Whyever not?

First Fish We got a glimpse of your lovely cargo by the way. What an incredible beauty, even if her nose is a bit out of joint.

Fitz the Faithful Really? I hadn't noticed.

Second Fish Oh yes. But we know her, don't we?

First Fish Oh yes, we know her alright.

Fitz the Faithful Do you?

Second Fish Yes. Of course she's in much better nick now than she was when we knew her. She was a laugh in those days. We used to push her about in her wheelchair through the shopping centres collecting chocolate bars from the old ladies. A great kid she was, though a bit of a stinker, a child like that though is bound to have dirty habits, it's just a matter of keeping your distance, but you know all this –

Fitz the Faithful No, I hadn't –

First Fish Oh, ha, ha! Love is blind, deaf and has no sense of smell.

Fitz the Faithful She's lovely, she smells like a rose.

Second Fish Things have changed –

First Fish – grown in compost, then.

Fitz the Faithful The poor girl! Leave her alone.

Second Fish   Oops. She can't help it, no, no of course, quite right.

First Fish   Careful with her though, –

Fitz the Faithful   What?

Second Fish   You know what we mean.

Fitz the Faithful   Eh?

First Fish   Don't slam into her too hard, she might snap.

Fitz the Faithful   This is monstrous. Get out of my way.

Second Fish   No, wait, you don't seem to quite understand.

First Fish   He doesn't understand.

Second Fish   It's us you have to answer to for her welfare.

Fitz the Faithful   Oh, why?

First Fish   Because we're her parents.

Fitz the Faithful   A couple of old men, two old fish swimming about, I don't think so.

Second Fish   You don't despise her lowly origins, we hope?

Fitz the Faithful   No, no. I only love her the more.

First Fish   Good, that's good. We paid for her treatment you know.

Fitz the Faithful   That's very kind of you, I'm sure.

Second Fish   Slaved and saved to keep her limbs straight; damn things used to curl like autumn leaves.

Fitz the Faithful   What can I say, you've done her proud.

First Fish   We knew some young buck would be grateful one day.

Fitz the Faithful   Yes thanks very much, now if you don't mind, I can't tread water all day.

Second Fish   Can't you?

Fitz the Faithful   Well no, of course not.

Second Fish   Oh that's odd because I would have thought anyone hitched up to her would be well practised in tramping about getting nowhere.

Fitz the Faithful   Very funny.

First Fish   We're not half as funny as she can be.

Fitz the Faithful   I suppose you're going to tell me about it.

Second Fish   There was the time she squeezed a little birdie fallen out of its nest until it oozed out between her fingers in a bucket of water.

First Fish   Or there was the time up at the school house when she did the old recital on the stage and no one dared tell her she didn't have a singing voice.

Second Fish   She never was one for criticism.

First Fish   Did you ever see her in the long jump?

Fitz the Faithful   No. But I can imagine. I'd better get back to her now I left her in the rain.

Second Fish   That's nice. I suppose you think you're going to look after her, are you?

Fitz the Faithful   Yes, I'll take care of her, don't you worry about that.

Second Fish   Oh yes, yes that's very fine, isn't it?

First Fish   Very fine indeed.

Second Fish   But we took care of her too, didn't we?

First Fish   But it wasn't that easy.

Second Fish   In fact, we had to leave her in her wheelchair.

First Fish   She cracked one too many jokes.

Second Fish   And ate one too many bars of chocolate.

First Fish   Put the old sneer on us once too often.

Second Fish   So we left her laughing away to herself at the shopping centre.

First Fish   So if you say to us you're going to look after her

Second Fish   We don't believe a word of it

First Fish   Because she's a difficult girl.

Second Fish   Very difficult person indeed.

First Fish   Behind her dark looks is a total blackness.

Second Fish   Bless her.

First Fish   So you'll be dumping her sooner or later.

Second Fish   And good riddance.

First Fish   You'll be well shot of her.

Second Fish   Let some other bugger pay the price.

First Fish   In fact as soon as you like, put her in a taxi and send her back to us.

Second Fish   Yes, we haven't seen her in ages.

Fitz the Faithful   Oh yes. And what will you do with her?

First Fish   We'll take her out to dinner as usual won't we?

Second Fish   Yes. She eats like a horse. Dobbin we call her.

Fitz the Faithful   Poor Dobbin. I love her.

First and Second Fish   (*together*) WE LOVE HER!

First Fish   But that doesn't help

Second Fish   Does it?

On the shore of the lake

Girl   So you're back at last. You're late. Did you get them?

Fitz the Faithful *throws down a sack with objects in it.*

Girl   Well. And what about the fish, what did you give them this time?

Fitz the Faithful   I gave them a few old stories for their collection, about when I was a little boy. I told them about my pets and er . . . my sporting prowess, and my singing ability.

Girl   That was a thrill for them. And what did they give you?

Fitz the Faithful   Well, they gave me a few pointers about yourself actually.

Girl   What do they know!

Fitz the Faithful   For a couple of old fish, quite a lot. They were full of admiration, said you were a great wit.

Girl   Is that all?

Fitz the Faithful   Of course, physically they said you were a masterpiece.

Girl   Mm.

Fitz the Faithful   Morally and emotionally too they said you'd overcome a great deal. Money well spent, I think was what they said.

Girl   What else?

Fitz the Faithful   Your virtuosity and intelligence were mentioned. They said that neither were at all overrated, and that in your home town they were . . . second to none there. They predicted you'd be a big superstar, earn lots of money and be a great literary figure with your novel when you finish it.

Girl   Anything else?

Fitz the Faithful   Great things too were expected of you in the hurdles.

Girl   Right. Now, shall we be getting on, I'm getting arthritis.

Fitz the Faithful   You don't know when you're liked.

Girl   Oh yes I do. I know when people tell me. They usually say I'm adorable.

Fitz the Faithful   What people were they?

Girl   I tried keeping a score in ink on my leg, but even *my* legs weren't long enough for that, look.

Fitz the Faithful   It's incredible.

Girl   I know.

In the Palace of King Cnut.

Cnut   I never thought the day would come when I wouldn't rejoice to see you. Why did you run away on our wedding day?

Girl   What better day? At least then I knew whatever future I found would be forever in your memory, and dedicated to you.

Cnut   I see.

Girl   You seem blind to that.

Cnut   Blindness is my only comfort.

Girl   If you knew how I had to drive myself away. I saw the distant hill from my window while they dressed me for the ceremony and I knew that although your deadly enemy lived on that volcano in the sea – I couldn't offer myself to you before I had climbed that hill, at whatever cost. I didn't want our marriage to be a fortress of fear, I wanted to be your best soldier, your bravest man at arms. Perhaps you prefer a dead chicken?

Cnut   But you didn't slay my enemy. You loved him.

Girl   I loved him first, then slew him. You'll find him dragging himself across the marshes in search of me. But it's not my name on his parched lips you'll find but yours. You don't believe me, but I've heard it, pursuing us on our way here, like the croaking of a hundred frogs. It surrounded us in the mist, and I thought to myself; there is my husband's triumph if he would hear it.

Cnut   This is all wrong.

Girl Wrong? More is wrong than just this. What worse disaster could befall a general than to see his riders returning victorious home from a battle he'd given up as lost?

Cnut You think I should have come knocking on that old bandit's door for you myself?

Girl You sent this adventurer for me and now I must ride off with him. Just think how happy we could have been now – me clinging around your neck, you racing across the meadow with your recaptured bride.

Cnut You talk of marshes and meadows. You think perhaps I don't know them. After this they can be my only home. I'm suddenly thirsty. If there's a mist out there tonight, I'll drink it. Shoot my horse, buckle my shoe, you may keep my hat, I'll not wear one. Now, where's the door? Good, good, open it.

He goes.

Fitz the Faithful He went off quick. He's driven to distraction, poor man. Don't you feel sorry for him, won't you call him back?

Girl Call him back? He deserted me, now he's gone off looking for sympathy.

Fitz the Faithful I hope he finds some. If you'd not left him this never would have happened.

Girl I would have been like a jar of unopened honey on his shelf.

*   *   *

The two are reclining together on a sofa.

Girl I think I may have led you astray. You're too young for me.

Fitz the Faithful How can you tell?

Girl You never ask me any questions. You have that total lack of curiosity peculiar to the under twenty-threes. You accept everything and appreciate nothing.

Fitz the Faithful There are a couple of things I've wondered about. Those letters you write, there are always so many, but they're never to me.

Girl To you? The very idea! They are to my dear absent husband, whom I loved so much and who now wanders about like a madman all on account of me – of course I write to him.

Fitz the Faithful I think he can do without your letters.

Girl Oh you do do you? *You* clearly can't. Perhaps you'd like to hear one, I keep them by me at all times. 'Dear husband, king of my heart, I spurned you and threw you out, and by God you deserved it. You cowardly creeping dishonest insect. How dare you drag me back and forth across the water when you know I hate travelling, how dare you plague me with your depression to embroil me in the slow suicide attempt you call your life? Life's not the word for it – you seemed to have a tryst with a double, a doppelganger inside you who controlled your very eyelids. He seemed to be threatening you with something, what was it? What awful secret? Idiot. You had no secret. God how I fought to preserve my existence. Now it delights and revives my soul to pay you back for all my suffering. But I am driven to distraction missing you and I wish for nothing more than to have you here again – no, to be out there with you eating roots in the forest and to thirst with you, to be like animals together, like hogs perhaps, or two tiny insects under a log in the darkness forever, our two time-blackened souls –

Fitz the Faithful   That's enough. It's best we set out immediately. We'll find him. God knows the man was in no state to go far. Wherever he is we'll throw ourselves at his mercy and repent, truly repent.

Girl   You don't repent, you just want someone to comfort you for your mistakes. But alright though, if you insist, we'll go and hunt for him. There's no point staying here a moment longer. And who knows darling, if we don't find my husband, we may find the solution to our troubles together instead.

Fitz the Faithful   Hah! Your offer of hope is no more a life line than a rope from a harpoon.

In the forest.

Cnut *and* **Ryan** *crawling like two bears following their breaths in the forest. They meet facing each other.*

Cnut   I think we've done this before.

Ryan   Never, we never did this before.

Cnut   Surely, that time you stole away my bride and we met like two bears following our breaths in the forest?

Ryan   That's this time you're talking about.

Cnut   It seems so familiar. Tell me, what power does she have over you?

Ryan   All power, today. Tomorrow, who knows, she'll have no power at all, I'll have forgotten her, but today I need her as much as food and water.

Cnut   I was trying to recreate the smell of her breath with my own against this piece of wood, when I was greeted with the foul stench of your rotten jaws. How did she bear it?

Ryan   She said you dressed yourself in roses and garlands of all kinds but you still stank, the way you capered about thinking you were gay and sweet was heart-rending. Your lumpenness, your sense of rotten manhood, your careful words, the begging, pleading tone in your voice. Let me be sick. Bleah. (*He retches.*)

Cnut   It's lies. I was never humble. She swore I was the sweetest dandy in the world.

Ryan   She swore on her chastity perhaps.

Cnut   I forgive her that you fool. In my time I . . . I . . . Oh help me!

Ryan   Look at it like this. She was no fun in the end remember. What did she ever deliver that was useful? I slept all through it you know. She did nothing for me. A man like me, a man mountain, a man monster like me, I slept, ate and went to the toilet three times before I remembered I was meant to be feasting on her gaze in my little cave-like tabernacle with its little beddy – I'm a busy fella. I get tired in the evenings from the sea air, I dropped off and before I knew it this pipsqueak fellow was tugging at me but all I wanted was to get back to my dream, my dream of her. I dreamed I was a young dandy not unlike the kind you wish you were, except young and handsome and fresh, a fool for all the world, she was hanging from my neck like a baboon and I was saying 'tomorrow we'll stay in bed and dream, I'll dream my dream of you, the one where I'm a dandy young and handsome and fresh, a fool for all the world, and you're hanging from my neck like a baboon and I'll say tomorrow we'll stay in bed and dream the dream of – '

Cnut   Oh shut up.

Ryan   There she was in my arms. I was like a farm-hand yoked to his plough in his ecstasy for all the world. Such slavery. Never before have I seen such beauty. Then I woke, this pipsqueak rattling my chains. Oh the terrible freedom of being awake, I could crush that gnat in his boots. Let's sleep, you and I in this grotto, come on let's snuggle up, it's so cold being awake, so lonely. Let's sleep the sleep of men, real men, men who have dispensed with love. And if one day our passions are too much for us to bear, we'll fight each other and knock each other down. Or we'll go and find treasure, store up money for our old age, what do you say?

Cnut   You're probably wondering why I chose her, a girl like that, hardly suitable company for a great king such as I. But I didn't choose her, it was an accident. I was out and about in my little kingdom making contact. Was that vanity? Quite possible. I am a vain man. I went into a bar, and she was the hatcheck girl, and she with her beautiful ways appealed to my vanity, I remember thinking she could be a problem to me, I saw it in the little pulsation above her lip. She was nervous naturally, her personality was written all over her face, and now mine is written all over the walls.

In the forest.

Fitz the Unfaithful   Stand back, stand back! I am Fitz. Fitz the gambler, Fitz the highwayman, Fitz the bastard.

Fitz the Faithful   Then Fitz my friend you have met your equal.

Fitz the Unfaithful   Who are you?

Fitz the Faithful   Don't you recognize me, brother? I was in love in these woods once; these ditches are as familiar to me as the ducts in my own heart. You want to rob me – here is my purse, empty. You want to run me through – here is my heart, no blood left.

Fitz the Unfaithful   Take your boots off you imbecile, before I blow your head off. Where is the lady in question, I may want to rape her.

Fitz the Faithful   She's behind you. Rape would be pointless now. She lies buried under that hill. She died of love, now the worms have their pleasure with her. Your contribution would, I feel, go unnoticed.

Fitz the Unfaithful   Straight from the heart my brother but not true, for there she sits as beautiful as ever on a stone. I think she may be smiling at me. Why is that? Can it be you've lost her? What possessed you to pretend she was dead? Perhaps you knew that she were better dead than be the girl she is. Was he right, princess?

Girl   You know he's always right.

Fitz the Unfaithful   Yes he is. That's a mystery he can best solve himself.

Girl   Sorry Fitz, I'm destined to love him too. He has such big brown eyes, and then there's that gap between his teeth. I'm fatally attracted to physical beauty. I must follow my destiny.

Fitz the Faithful   And me? What destiny can a man have alone in the forest of mirrors?

Girl   Oh you really can, I promise you. Think about your bad luck. It's kind of a living death, almost like love itself, only more so.

Fitz the Faithful   Have you no consolation to offer me?

Girl   Yes, think how faithful to you I will be in your absence. I shall long for you every night and wish we'd never said goodbye.

Fitz the Faithful   I . . .

Girl   Is there something you want to say?

Fitz the Faithful   We look so similar, Fitz and I.

Girl   Yes but you're not quite twins, are you? Goodbye, farewell.

Cnut *and* **Ryan** *in the forest.* **Fitz the Faithful** *comes into view.*

Cnut   And what's this? You're that dreadful Fitz the Unfaithful who's been robbing everyone and making a nuisance of himself to the young women.

Fitz the Faithful   No, no, not I.

Cnut   Yes your are, in fact I remember hearing you once attempted something unspeakable upon the golden princess of the slender heart, my wife, poor little girlie.

Fitz the Faithful   No you've got me mixed up with my twin brother. I am Fitz the Faithful.

Ryan   A likely story.

Fitz the Faithful   Yes I have been roaming this forest looking for you, if indeed you are the old king, you look like nothing at all. I set out with your wife but she left me. My brother had that old demonic smile, she didn't trouble to resist 'Love', she said 'is my inspiration'. She liked his gappy teeth, she liked his walk, she said he sometimes had dark sultry looks in his brown eyes, sometimes like a film starlet, sometimes like Genghis Khan. 'I'd give my husband's kingdom for a sofa and a teapot and a packet of biscuits and a TV. I'd sit with him on my knee all Saturday afternoon, you know, a kiss, a fondle, a little snooze, another kiss, his sweet young breast beneath his favourite jersey and then a sudden path of kisses all across the meadows and marshes, such beauty I never did behold,' she said.

Pause. They all muse dejectedly.

Cnut   Time to go, I think; we two are off somewhere, perhaps to drown. It's the end, life will go on without us. Evidently. What's left? Did you ever hear such a thing?

Ryan   No, no I never did.

Fitz the Faithful   Well, tell you what, I'll join you. I'll follow you to the water's edge.

Ryan   Oh no, no, no, no. No, no, no, no. Oh no. You see, the Executioner, I've paid him. He has the golden chopper.

Fitz the Faithful   Does he?

Cnut   Yes. Mr Ryan. Out with your old golden chopper. Your green golden chopper. Chop off his head.

Ryan   Lovers die in the forest.

Fitz the Faithful   You think I wouldn't be content to die in that way. Without that girl, what will I do? Have little chats like this with old men? Or ride off and seek a fortune? Write a book? A man denied food isn't going to set the table for others to eat from. I could run away you see but I don't. I'm too sleepy but even dreaming of her won't help because I will wake up so I'd gladly let you execute me. And yet what is it all about? An average enough girl, beautiful it's true, although her beauty sometimes conceals a great crudity in her features. Charming? I'm sure that wears off once you get to know her. Clever, perhaps – but below average, unless you count her enigmatic vacancy. Honest? Inspired? Holy? these she keeps carefully hidden.

Ryan   A dull girl from a suburb in fact.

Fitz the Faithful   Perhaps, and if I were to now list her *faults*, I think you'd agree my love for her must be of the purest kind to overlook them.

Ryan   What are they?

Fitz the Faithful   Moody selfish lazy, slow. A hypocrite though she's careful to avoid all situations of sufficient contrast to reveal it, she lives in a monochrome, monotone, she used to wrestle with the cupboard every night to fix it in her small room, but it would be broken again by morning, this was her chief amusement. She walks like a cross between Brigitte Bardot and a paraplegic hurdler dragging her left foot in a manner that delights the small boys that follow her behind. She towers over them like a monstrous Venus. But I wouldn't say she can't be affectionate, and in fact given half the chance she'll hang like a monkey from your neck presenting herself to you in such a way that you are like a yoked ploughman in his ecstasy for all the world.

Cnut   And her smile?

Fitz the Faithful   Ah now, there!

Ryan   Sounds fatal. You're better off dead.

They chop off his head.

In the Hermit's cave – **Cnut** *and* **Ryan,** **Girl** *and* **Fitz the Unfaithful**

Cnut   You're just in time, I'm about to give my last bit of advice to lovers before my friend and I go off in search of a hoard of treasure.

Girl   I hope you have good luck.

Cnut   Luck? We ought to. We've hoarded and hoarded all our lives, by God we ought to be able to find some of it. What is success and power for anyway if not to promote good luck upon this earth, if not to project us away into oblivion with necklaces of gold between our fingers, eh Mr Ryan?

Ryan   Are you going to tell the little sister all our deadly secrets?

Cnut   Don't think we've always been hermits you know. You might once in your youth (excuse me mademoiselle) have seen me striding arm in arm with some of the most angelic divinities of women on earth, and they used to whisper in my ear 'I'm still totally and utterly in love with you for all that you're a cantankerous old philanderer amusing yourself at my expense' and

I'd look into their eyes in my dreamy way and say, 'It's my mission to teach you about the sore elbow of love, the misery and failure clothed in wisdom and my awful handsomeness.' God, that never failed to get a rise out of them, the little darlings. They thought I was only fooling with them but in the end I lost my shirt, didn't I Mr Ryan?

Ryan   You lost your big knickers too, I'd say.

Cnut   That's it, lost my big knickers too. I lost my throat and my thumb and my other parts, one of which developed a funny smell and nearly fell off, didn't it, Mr Ryan?

Ryan   Didn't it just?

Cnut   Because I never was fooling, no not really. There was one I remember, she had a dark little snarl on her at the best of times and one day I put my foot right into it – I stumbled on my galoshes if you get my meaning and well, she stripped me down right enough, tore the sky from over me and dug the ground up from beneath my feet and threw me into the hole, and marched off leaving me for dead, returning moments later for her bus-fare, her face contorted with pain as she said 'I'm going to get me some good action somewhere else 'cause this stinks.' and that's what she did, the little darling, and who can blame her. But the wag of the tail is this: she walked right smack-bang into a wall, didn't she Mr Ryan?

Ryan   You put it how you like.

Cnut   Right smack-bang into a wall and I won't say I laughed but whether it was now that she fell under it or climbed up and fell off it, the point is she's food for the birds now and it'll teach her for being blind to criticism, not like I was you see because I was always a damn good listener.

Ryan   That's it. You shouldn't be taken in by the talk.

Cnut   No, don't be taken in by that. It's a point of modesty for me, to listen wisely and speak like a fool.

Girl   Anyhow, my problem is, I feel I've walked right smack-bang into a wall.

Cnut   I see. And what kind of a wall would that be if I may enquire?

Girl   Well, it's difficult to tell. It could be a wall of experience, or a wall of repetition.

Ryan   Same thing . . .

Girl   Or a wall of my kind of . . .

Cnut   Your kind of . . .

Girl My kind of love. My kind of repetition and experience, my love of repetition and my kind of experience, which is one of love and then repetition. Because what's the point of falling in love when it's only going to be a wall?

Cnut It's repetitious.

Girl It's more than repetitious.

Cnut What is it?

Girl First it's love, then it's repetition, then it's a wall.

Cnut So that's your kind of love.

Girl Yes!

Cnut You've got a problem.

Girl I know.

Cnut What do you think causes this?

Girl It's caused I think by my never ending search for variety.

Cnut I see.

Girl Variety, new experience, a different kind of love.

Cnut You don't like your own kind of love?

Girl No. I want another kind.

Cnut Where do you hope to find it?

Girl In others.

Cnut Not in yourself?

Girl Of course not. But the more I search the more I get the same thing.

Cnut From others?

Girl No. From myself. And then from others.

Cnut Naturally you feel frustrated. Your potential is being wasted.

Girl I have such love in my heart.

Cnut You seem to have, yes.

Girl First there was my husband-to-be. In his youth, so he told me, he was so striking girls used to literally fall at his feet. Girls, just like me, he said – young, passionate, graceful, and a mite mysterious and enigmatic they all behaved the same way, so what could I do but follow suit? Of course I adore that kind of thing. I've always given satisfaction when I've done it, because of the great emotion in me, so overwhelming is it, I feel pity for the very feet I kiss. In fact I remember he put out his hand to stop me 'Stop' he said, 'get back', but it was like trying to stop the wind or the rain. 'It's no good' I said, 'the tide of my passion will engulf you and you can't stop it' and sure enough within a few short weeks he was offering me babies, villas, hotels, a little pied-à-terre in town, so I said 'marry me, meet me at the staion we'll go to Gretna Green.' 'No need,' he said, 'I've taken out a loan and bought my own little chapel with gothic seating, most commodious.' I couldn't refuse because I love architecture of all kinds. And besides, he was the king of my heart, the prince of my person. Already, I hoped to have a little prince of my own in my belly, I had tried to squeeze it out of him, but he was a born politician, a weigher and a juggler but an amateur juggler, for though he lived a double life, he refused to live a double life. He was too busy being pursued by a stranger within him, so I took that as my cue and on the morning of my wedding while the old biddies were squeezing my stays I spied across the bay the ruin of my next love, another piece of architecture, a pile on a rock, and I was away.

Cnut   A great story. But what does it prove? For if he had said 'yes platform six, 9.30', you would have overslept and let him down and then; if you'd arrived later, maybe let's say six hours later, and he'd been waiting but happened to have popped off to the loo at the moment before you arrived, you would have taken one look at the empty station, tossed your beautiful head and gone off in a huff.

Girl   And well justified I should say, I won't tolerate rudeness.

Cnut   Well young man, what do you say to all this? You've been very quiet.

Fitz the Unfaithful   Humph.

Cnut   Yes very quiet, grinning at me through the gaps in your teeth.

Fitz the Unfaithful   I can't help it if I'm lucky.

Cnut   He he he! Let me shake your hand boy.

Fitz the Unfaithful   Don't mind, alright. Shake away.

Cnut   So this is the new man. He looks like a walking jinx.

Girl   Oh, him.

Fitz the Unfaithful   Would you tell your secrets to a girl whose only subject of conversation is her ex-boyfriends?

Girl   Next is that big brave man-monster on the rock who boldly welcomed me as a fugitive from his hated enemy, my husband-to-be. He bore me away in his arms and gave me bread and jam. 'Making love with you' he said 'is a bit of a mystery, you keep leaving the room'. I never told him the reason why I had to keep leaving the room, 'Are you shy?' he said, so sweet of him to be concerned. 'Are you in pain?' he said. Pain never put me off. 'Are you . . . in love?' he asked finally. What could I say? I never knew if he meant with him or with someone else. After that, I left the room every few minutes, I couldn't stop. Until in the end we sat either side of the door, listening for each other's footsteps in terror. The night raged on about us – full of unanswered questions. It was a dark tempest, blacker than black. You couldn't see a thing.

Cnut   Well, Mr Ryan, what do you say to that little lot?

Ryan   Just a few questions . . . this man-monster, as you call him. A sensitive type was he?

Girl   I was astonished how sensitive he was. First he was sitting the other side of the room, with his back to me on the floor, from which position his muscular beauty could only just be glimpsed. Then there was the bread and jam he made, so slowly and deliberately I thought he'd never get it done, then he started moving about in the dark, and really there was no telling what he'd do next. I'd glimpse him standing on a chair, then hear him under the bed, then over against the wall muttering to himself or singing some obscure song in a high-pitched drone. It was like being in a room with a Venus and Adonis together in one, acting out their own little affair for my benefit. I really was moved.

Ryan   And what about the warmth of his massive body? And his great arms?

Girl   I promise you, when I saw the white flash of his flanks glancing in the moonlight, tears came to my eyes, and the red scars of all the cruel wounds on his breast I wanted to build a shrine for him in my embrace.

Ryan   And what went wrong?

Girl   I had a few letters to write. It really is important not to lose your concentration, isn't it?

Ryan   So they say.

Girl   I did my best, but by then I sensed his heart wasn't in it. He cried out a few times and I could see the characteristic sweat on his upper lip, and the expression of excruciation on his face certainly aroused my curiosity but it turned out I had my elbow in his solar-plexus; the poor man was in pain, his battle wound started playing him up and we had to unscrew his wooden leg, and by that time I was so confused what with his beauty on the one hand and my reluctance to seize it for my own on the other – you see, I think we would have been a great pair together. We could have taught each other a thing or two.

Ryan   Don't you see, the old clodhopper was too old to learn?

Girl   Probably. I was certainly too young. And thus we parted. Helped of course by that swine FitzGibbon.

Ryan   The swine!

Cnut   The swine!

Girl   This imposter, whom I shall never forgive, turned up claiming to be an emissary from my dear husband – I was completely taken in. Naturally I went with him but of course it turned out he wanted me all for himself at which point I cut off all contact as soon as possible, after of course he had ferried me about a bit and led me through the forest to you.

Ryan   He got what he deserved.

Girl   At first you see, it was talk, talk, talk, I couldn't get a word in. It was monstrous. Not a bit of it made any sense. Then he lured me into my room, did wonderful things to me, fulfilled my every wish from his soft lips down to his garters until I had to call a halt. This has gone too far I said, buttoning my suit, and sitting in an armchair. It's no good I said, enticing me with your many charms your honesty originality and intelligence nor is it altogether fair to give me long paranoid lectures about the universe and nearly scare the life out of me, and then just when I feel safe, to turn up in your beautiful suit of clothes and your white thighs making yourself irresistible in that under the counter way, when I have much to fear from such liaisons.

Cnut   What would your husband say?

Girl   Exactly. He expects high standards from me. I have my reputation to think of.

Cnut   I'm sure you do. You're very well known.

Girl   I'm very well known and when it comes to love I'm very well known for my –

Cnut   Your –

Girl   I have some difficulties of course. I'm not afraid of difficulties. I'm known for them, I expect them. The last thing I need is that . . .

Cnut   Bimbo.

Girl   That bimbo-imposter.

Cnut   Bimbo-imposter-peddlar.

Girl   Peddling his wares with such large quantities of understanding, his drunkard's dream. Who needs it? I don't.

Pause.

No. I need this man. Fitz the Unfaithful.

Cnut   What? Is he that infamous stealer of hearts and purses?

Girl   Yes that's right. Fitz the Bastard. My guardian angel.

They leave.

Edge of the forest, a river-beach.

Girl Where are we going?

Fitz the Unfaithful I've put up with you long enough. I want to get back to civilisation.

Girl Do you think we'll get married. Will we have a 3-day party where I can invite all my friends?

Fitz the Unfaithful Your lip is beaded with sweat again. What does that indicate, I've been wondering?

Girl It means I expect you're going to make me give you all my jewels and necklaces and my letters.

Fitz the Unfaithful Oh yes, I don't suppose you have all that on you now, do you?

Girl Yes, of course.

Fitz the Unfaithful Hand it all over then.

Girl Do you insist?

Fitz the Unfaithful Of course.

Girl Here, then.

Fitz the Unfaithful Good.

Girl What are you going to give me in return?

Fitz the Unfaithful Nothing.

Girl What've you brought me to this old river-beach for? It stinks.

Fitz the Unfaithful That is where I work.

Girl But I thought you were a robber.

Fitz the Unfaithful On high days, but mostly I just pick up things people leave. Lovers come down here to hide and I pick up the buckles they pull off each other's pants, and trample into the mud. Keys or sometimes lockets or golden rings get pulled off and thrown away in a temper or sometimes two rings tied together and chucked out a little way in a secret marriage. It's being going on for centuries and all I have to do is dig down deep enough.

Girl I see. You're a scavenger.

Fitz the Unfaithful That's right.

Girl That's not very exciting.

Fitz the Unfaithful No, it isn't, but I find the mud very amusing. Don't you? Or when the mist rolls up on a low tide you sometimes see some interesting things.

Girl   I can't see anything. You're pretty much set in your ways down here, aren't you?

Fitz the Unfaithful   (*he's busy picking up something from the mud*) Oh, a red rose.

Girl   What's that, look, an aeroplane landing on the water!

Fitz the Unfaithful   That's not an aeroplane.

Girl   Oh no. No, it's a boat!

Fitz the Unfaithful   That's not a boat either.

Girl   What is it then?

Fitz the Unfaithful   All I can see is a couple of old fish jumping.

Girl   Oh.

Fitz the Unfaithful   Yes, just a couple of old fish, although, they do seem to be waving.

The Hermit's Cave.

Cnut *and* **Ryan** *in the forest.* **Fitz the Unfaithful** *comes into view.*

Cnut   Oh look, here comes another one. Seems as if we might have got the wrong man.

Ryan   Well well well young man, aren't you Fitz the Unfaithful who's being making a nuisance of himself to all the young ladies and even –

Fitz the Unfaithful   Please, don't speak to me now old man, I need to be alone.

Cnut   Oh? Tears? Real tears?

Ryan   It's a sad day when a treacherous cuthroat starts weeping: because he can expect no sympathy.

Cnut   Has the cutpurse had his heart strings snipped by any chance?

Pause.

Ryan   Oh dear, it seems he has. That's a lesson to you boy. You shouldn't use your heart like a purse and try to fill it up with a store of gold, greedy, greedy, greedy.

Cnut   Yes that goodlooking head of yours has got you into trouble hasn't it. My little barmaid and then my wife, who else I wonder? A string of women, a necklace of beauties. I think he's even conquered his own wayward heart and fallen in love with himself.

Ryan   Lie down here and tell us all about it. That's it, put your head on this block of wood as if it's a pillow, and tell your two old uncles all about it.

Cnut   Now, was it her matchless beauty made you sad?

Fitz the Unfaithful   No, she had a broken nose and the wheelchair blues which kept me happy.

Ryan   Was it her sweet nature and her generosity which made you so sorrowful?

Fitz the Unfaithful   No, her mean streak and her sneer kept me safe from that.

Cnut   Was it her mind, her ready wit and her understanding brought you so low?

Fitz the Unfaithful   No, because she never admitted to understanding a word I said.

Ryan   That was cunning of her.

Cnut   Was it that she forgave you the weaknesses in your nature?

Fitz the Unfaithful   No, she even blamed me for the weaknesses in hers. She didn't miss a thing.

Ryan   Was it the way her breadth of experience, coupled with her perception and the skylark liberty of her way of thinking made her so full of mercy and a kind of divine and passionate pity?

Fitz the Unfaithful   No.

Cnut   Was it the gentle touch of her hands upon you that lured you into this despair?

Fitz the Unfaithful   No, thank God, she never touched me otherwise who knows where I'd be.

Ryan   Then, what has the girl done.

Fitz the Unfaithful   She let me go.

Cnut and Ryan   Oh.

Fitz the Unfaithful   She gave me all the love I could take and said I didn't deserve it and better not cast my shadow upon her again because I was never the man she thought I was, neither as bad as my reputation nor as good as she required and would I please leave at once, and I was free to die or live on, as whatever and with whomever I wanted and she'd never think of me more for the disappointment would make her annoyed and spoil her day, her life, her mood, her looks and her appetite.

But are there better men than me? I asked incredulous.
I'm banking on it, she said.

And as she said this the smallest of tears squeezed into her narrowing eyes and I swear that if a volcano had opened up I would have cast myself into it – to burn away the memory of the regret I felt or, if she had thrown herself into it in search of this bankable other I would have jumped in after her and been her guide, a Virgil to her Dante in hell looking for a male Beatrice perched on a piece of brimstone.

Cnut How touching. How heroic. Here's true love at last awkwardly nestling in a villainous heart. Who'd have guessed? And if you would have found this magazine husband?

Fitz the Unfaithful I would have taken my sword and cut off his –

They cut off his head.

Ryan and Cnut Head.

In the Forest.

The two men are down a hole. They've been digging for treasure.

Girl Hello? Is anybody there?

Ryan Look! A nice young girlie.

Cnut Hello sweetie. What are you doing out in the Forest of Mirrors so late and dark?

Girl I'm looking for my dearest and latest lover. I sent him away and now I regret it.

Cnut Mm.

Girl I think I may have hurt his feelings. I *know* I've hurt his feelings. Surprisingly he turned out to be a bit sensitive.

Cnut Well it's never too late to say sorry.

Girl Oh I don't want to say sorry, I still mean every word of it. He deserved it. He's a terrible disappointment to me, as a person, you know. In fact, I no longer think of him as a person.

Cnut But?

Girl But I'm still totally and utterly in love with him.

Cnut You'd like to make him happy.

Girl Yes.

Cnut Perhaps you can correct him?

Girl Yes.

Cnut Teach him by your good example.

Girl Yes.

Cnut   If only you could find him.

Girl   Yes.

Cnut   What if you pushed him too far?

Girl   Mm.

Cnut   Pushed him right up to the brink.

Girl *sighs.*

Cnut   He may have lost his head.

Girl   Sometimes I do say things, some things I *don't* really mean. Or rather I say them as an expression of my love.

Cnut   I see.

Girl   You have to distinguish between passion and considerateness don't you?

Cnut   Yes.

Girl   It would be silly just being nice to someone you really love.

Cnut   Ridiculous.

Girl   When I love someone I want to probe them right to their bone marrow, and the closer I look at all their failings the more passionately I love them. In fact I end up loving them for their failings, apart of course for the ones that make them a non-person and then I just reject, well I have to. Because a non-person always tries to make you into one too, to keep him company I suppose, maybe he's lonely in his grimy little world. I mean we all want to be understood don't we, implicitly, but to understand you have to know, and you can't know what is morally repugnant to you. You can only ignore it at best. Don't you think?

Cnut   Yes. Ignorance is the best policy.

Girl   Or you can know and then suddenly not know, you can forget. And from forgetting comes forgiving and once you're forgiven you can love again.

Cnut   Ignore, forget, forgive, love again.

Girl   That's it.

Cnut   All you have to do is find him.

Girl   Yes.

Cnut   And maybe he's looking for you?

Girl   Do you think so?

Cnut   And if he isn't, someone else might be. There are other fish in the sea.

Girl   I'm banking on it.

Cnut   Someone more suitable, even.

Girl   Do you think so?

Cnut   Yes, someone more like you.

Girl   Mm, possible.

Cnut   Someone who will appreciate you for your better points alone.

Girl   And this person, do you think they'll find me?

Cnut   They might. It all depends.

Girl   On what?

Cnut   If they know you.

Girl   – ?

Cnut   When they see you.

Ryan   Pass us that big sword will you.

Girl   This? What are you doing?

Ryan   Just digging.

She swings the sword round absently and their heads disappear.

Girl   Oops. Sorry.

Second Man   So, nearly all of them died in that hillside forest.

First Man   What a terrible tragedy. What happened to her?

Second Man   Her? Oh I don't think anyone like that ever really existed.

First Man   Oh.

Second Man   But remember Fitz the Unfaithful? Well, weeks later, after beeing food for the birds, he came accidentally back to life again.

First Man   Oh really?

Second Man   Yes, well, minus one arm and one foot, and an ear, but nevertheless alive, but a ghostly terrible figure that struck horror into all that saw him.

Fitz the Unfaithful   I've said goodbye to this world once. What a terrible wrench to find myself still here, this is no longer my home. To die is to die. I thirst for death. Ah that word DEATH, it is like water to my soul.

Second Man   Just at that undead moment, a young woman calls out to him, stops him.

Young Woman   Hey you! Are you sober enough to be able to find a door key in this darkness? I've dropped mine.

Fitz the Unfaithful   You wouldn't believe it, you just wouldn't believe it, what a time to ask me!!

Young Woman   Oh God, look, forget it.

Fitz the Unfaithful   No, no I'll look, I'll find it, you know, just so that I can congratulate myself on my way home. Now, what did it look like?

Young Woman   A key, just like a key.

Fitz the Unfaithful   Right.

They look, she half-heartedly, incapable.

Young Woman   I've had a beautiful evening. I wish I could tell someone about it.

Fitz the Unfaithful   Why don't you?

Young Woman   Christ it was the night of my life I reckon, the *best* night, you know what I mean?

Fitz the Unfaithful   Whereabouts did you drop it?

Young Woman   Just here. Look you don't have to, it's very kind and that, but – I think I'm in love, I think my life has begun at last! I just hope it still feels like that in the morning. Do you think it will? I used to think it didn't matter but recently I've been all . . . I don't know, tearful, crying for no reason. So tonight I fell in love. I had no real reason really, but just to save my soul. Is that a good enough reason to fall in love?

Fitz the Unfaithful   I must sit down.

Young Woman   Because I think if I don't do it now I'll be left in a void forever, I'll end up on my own.

First Man   That was an odd little story.

Second Man   Look would you excuse me a moment I have to make a phone call.

First Man   Sure.

Second Man   (*on the phone*) Hello Mrs Chubb, I was wondering if I could speak to – has she, the 6.23? in at – Thank you Mrs Chubb, yes I will, an enormous green bag full of presents, I can imagine. I'll carry it . . . if I'm not too late. You had a nice Christmas then? Mr Chubb turned up to pay his respects? I bet Lou-Lou was pleased, poor little darling. You got her old wheelchair out of the loft? How did the? . . . Wheeled Mr Chubb about in it?? Oh, stumped his – fell down the . . . swelled to the size of a – water on the – never walk a – poor Mr – Dancing days are – yes. Well alright Mrs Chubb, I'd better – if I'm to meet Lou-Lou at the . . . yes, better not be . . .

or she'll . . . Yes you know what a, yes I do too Mrs Chubb, very dearly, I will look after her Mrs – Did she? Did she? Was she? Was she? all the time? Every night? Yes. Yes. What a – Did she? Broken her – ? Never be the same a – So do I. Yes that's why I don't want to miss her now at the – I do. I will I'm really . . . more than anything Mrs Ch – . I am yes – I do! – I do often – I'm crying *now* Mrs Chubb – I said I'm . . . I am yes. Yes, Yes I'm sorry Mrs . . . Did you? I'm sure that cheered her – No. No. I've always thought she – lots, – really. She – Yes, she. No I assume you mm – from what I've seen she – Mrs Chubb she has a wonderful appetite I wouldn't worry, normally yes. Well if she's upset . . . I will. But I'd better. If I'm . . . you know she . . . You know what's she's like . . . a toss of the head and off she . . . Please Mrs Chubb I think I'm going to faint . . . Don't want to make her wait. Yes. Yes. Goodbye Mrs (*Phone down.*) Damn. I'll never make it now.

Second Man   (*at the girl's door*) Lou-Lou, let me in. I miss you so much. It's all my fault, I take it all back, I wish we'd never parted, I can't remember your face. I've forgotten all your mannerisms, you took back your photo, I tore up your letters. I've nothing left. Everything we said to each other is slipping out of my mind. I've been talking to a friend about it and I've decided you were right after all, in the end, I was a fool, I treated you badly, I took it all for granted, I never gave you a chance, I was a coward, a liar, a cheat, I was unworthy, I patronised you, I was pompous and conceited, I wore the wrong shoes. But can't we just – I've decided it's not a bad thing for you all in all, at the end of the day I've decided it's beneficial, even though it will break your heart, I think it will be good for you, not like I said, not ruin you, but make you perhaps, so I think it's alright if we carry on for a little while longer and do all those things you said you'd planned for us to do, before I went and said it was all over.

Girl   Can't you say anything to make me feel better?

Second Man   Yes, Em. I think I'm afraid of you because I think you could be too much for me. You're too strong for me to resist, that's why I ran away and made up this awful story that I tell everyone, but it's all lies, it wasn't like that at all, really the truth is that you are a wonderful kind sweet intelligent perceptive girl with the heart and mind and body of a woman that bears your divine spirit about on this earth and you are entirely normal and straight and real and you have bravely outfaced the perverted challenge to your values, from this man-boy-deceiver-hero, who snatched it all away from you just as you were expanding your tolerance and your ambition and your appetite, but you see I have a wife and children a giant sugar plantation and a fish farm and a castle on the hill.

Girl   What did your friend say?

Second Man   She said: remember to have all the feelings. Don't be so considerate. You're not responsible for her life, after all. She said, phone her up, go round, wait outside her house at four in the morning. Tell her you love her and will never leave her. It sounds, she said, as if neither of you have got what you can out of it yet. Give it another go.

Girl So what have you decided to do?

Second Man To fall at your knees.

Girl I can't see it myself.

Second Man Look, here. (*He does so.*) Tell me you forgive me.

Girl Alright.

Second Man Louise, my sweetheart (*He falls tears onto her trainers.*) Now do you believe I love you?

Girl Yes. I believe you. But, no more fantasies. No more stories. We'll start with a clean slate. You must be dishonest to everyone else, but never to me.

Second Man Alright.

Girl No more exaggerating.

Second Man Yes, no more. Can we do those things you'd planned for us?

Girl Yes, I had planned some stuff. I was so looking forward to it. One thing was, I thought we'd go for a walk in a forest.

Second Man What?

She cuts off his head with a giant sword.

Gregory Motton questioned by Nick Drake

Q: Do you think a playwright should talk about his work?

A: It is certainly not important for a playwright to talk about his work. Anything he can say is likely to be limiting and reductive since whatever he wanted to say is presumably best expressed in the form he has said it in. Just as what anyone says about a work of art is not likely to be more than partly true or partly comprehensive; what a writer says about his own work is expected to be more definite than this, and so the actual shortcomings of his remarks are made worse by people's expectations.

It is a strange contradiction that while people are very keen to hear writers speak about their work, there is a common presumption that a playwright doesn't know what he has written.

Perhaps there is a longing to hear a work's scope reduced, on the authority of the writer himself.

Q: Is it useful or appropriate to ask a playwright questions about his plays?

A: It's often an excuse for people not to use their own judgement. The more they ask, the less they understand. What can there possibly be to ask? It's a way of avoiding the play. There is a habit of referring things to a higher authority while nothing is allowed to remain what it is, but rather has to be defined in terms of something else, in terms of ideas that are extraneous to the work itself, and important only because they are temporarily what is on people's minds. You could if you wished *judge* the *Kama Sutra* in terms of Victorian sexual morality, for example, but you'd probably not understand it too well and you certainly wouldn't get much out of it. Asking the playwright isn't trying to get to the root of the play, that lies in the play itself. It's just the same as asking a teacher or director, worse in fact. People will do anything to avoid what's in front of them. When someone asks me about a play I normally feel they are asking to be let off. What can you say? That play doesn't exist. It isn't really like that. This is what it's really like . . .

Q: How should we talk about plays?

A: I don't know if they are really something you'd want to talk about. Maybe talk about them if you don't get anything out of them.

Q: What is special about the form of drama for you?

A: All forms have limitations. The limitations are the liberation.

Q: Could you describe something of the way your plays come to be written?

A: I try to find the form, that is to say, the tone of what I want to write. By the time I've found it, the play is normally written.

Q: Do you have an idea of how your imagination works to create the play?

A: Imagination is a word I don't really understand in connection with writing. We all have what you could call imagination. It's like hope or fear; you hope there's some point getting up in the morning, you imagine your lunch will taste nice, you imagine your new shoes will make you look like someone else, you hope you'll kiss someone. It's creative energy. How do you picture yourself on your deathbed, or on the mountain top? Even if you want to see it all as endless and senseless you still have to imagine it being so. In terms of imagination, writing a play or a book or a poem is no different from what we all do, all the time.

Q: How does a play find its shape?

A: What is in it demands a form. If it has another form it would be something else. You can't force it to be otherwise. Sometimes you have to settle for a form that isn't very satisfying, that is to say a play that isn't very satisfying.

Q: What do you think is the relationship between ideas and imagination in plays?

A: What do you mean by ideas? Do you mean received ideas? Or how we define the contents of our own imaginations? Received ideas are likely to be in conflict with the contents of your imagination since your hopes and fears don't normally fit into someone else's. Sometimes you see plays that think they are about (received) ideas but in fact all you see is someone's fears and hopes running out of control. At other times, you see a play that is the definition of the contents of someone's imagination. You could call that play an idea.

Q: Are your plays and their characters a surprise to you?

A: No more than anything else about me is a surprise to me – hopefully rather less.

Q: Do you write in terms of characters and stories?

A: There are 'people' and stories in my plays. They don't write the play though, I write the play.

Q: What would you say to a group of young actors working on *The Forest of Mirrors*?

A: Don't let your expectations get the better of you. You don't have to interpret something. You have to let it be what it is, not what you want it to be, or what someone else says it is. A play isn't there as an opportunity for anyone to be especially creative. If someone, a director for example, wants that, they can write their own plays. And, you know that moment when something that has seemed vague and difficult suddenly becomes clear, when someone sheds light on it for you and the problems disappear and it all makes sense? Beware that moment.

Gregory Motton's first plays, performed in London at the Riverside Studios and the Royal Court, were *Chicken, Ambulance* and *Downfall*. Poetic and original, they explore the bleak, disconcerting and fragmentary experience of modern life with great humour and directness. 'His language sings with the poetry of unfulfilled love, abandoned souls and lost dreams.' *Guardian*. Gregory Motton's plays have also been widely produced in France, and hailed as 'masterpieces'. Likening his work to Beckett's, his recent French director said, 'He goes into things which aren't clear or certain and which can't be simplified; he explores complexity, contradiction, the enigmatic, the inexplicable.' Recent new work includes *Looking at You (Revived) Again, A Message for the Broken-Hearted*, and *The Terrible Voice of Satan* (Royal Court, 1993); and translations of several of Strindberg's plays for the Citizens' Theatre, Glasgow, and Opera Factory. His work for young people includes *Sleeping Beauty* for the Little Angel Marionette Theatre.

The Forest of Mirrors

Production Notes

Setting and staging

This is a fable which draws on, among other things, the legend of King
Canute (King Cnut). In *The Forest of Mirrors*, King Cnut is about to be
married, when his bride runs away. However, nothing is what it seems. Fitz
the Faithful and Fitz the Unfaithful might be brothers, or they might not. A
strange, surreal tale unfolds against a variety of backgrounds: the monster
Ryan's palace, King Cnut's castle, the shore of the lake, underwater, the
forest, and the hermit's cave.

Although the Forest of Mirrors reflects itself continuously, to design a set
actually incorporating mirrors would perhaps be needlessly obvious. The
audience will need to let the play's images and allusions sink in, and will not
want to be distracted by a set which 'over-explains' the company's
interpretation. It might be better to find a way to let the play speak for itself.

For example, **music** might be useful in creating space for reflection, but
should not interrupt the flow of the play.

Casting

There are two pairs of men:
Fitz the Faithful and Fitz the Unfaithful, King Cnut and Monster Ryan.
All four lose their heads, literally.

Other characters include:
Two old fish, who might 'double up' with First Man and Second Man.
A young woman.
A girl (around whom all the action takes place).

The girl is the key to understanding the play. She is in search of variety, and
a new kind of love. But the themes of repetition and reflection are in evidence
throughout her curious journey – she keeps coming across more of the same
from herself and from others. The demands of the sophisticated but
'unbaggaged' language of the play, suggest a need for a cast with considerable
maturity.

Questions

1. Why does the girl leave Cnut for his enemy?

2. What is the girl's attitude
   i   to love?
   ii   to herself?
   iii to loyalty?

3. How do the functions of the various characters change?

4. Who *are* the characters?

5. What do the various decapitations represent?

6. What might the forest represent?

7. To what extent are the men dependent on the girl?

Exercise

Explore the story of King Cnut, in history and legend. Identify how this, and other legends, have informed the play.

Suzy Graham-Adriani
Director/Producer for BT National Connections

Methuen Student Editions

Methuen Modern Plays

include work by

Jean Anouilh
John Arden
Margaretta D'Arcy
Peter Barnes
Brendan Behan
Edward Bond
Bertolt Brecht
Howard Brenton
Simon Burke
Jim Cartwright
Caryl Churchill
Noël Coward
Sarah Daniels
Nick Dear
Shelagh Delaney
David Edgar
Dario Fo
Michael Frayn
John Guare
Peter Handke
Jonathan Harvey
Declan Hughes
Terry Johnson

Barrie Keeffe
Stephen Lowe
Doug Lucie
John McGrath
David Mamet
Arthur Miller
Mtwa, Ngema & Simon
Tom Murphy
Peter Nichols
Joe Orton
Louise Page
Luigi Pirandello
Stephen Poliakoff
Franca Rame
David Rudkin
Willy Russell
Jean-Paul Sartre
Sam Shepard
Wole Soyinka
Theatre Workshop
Sue Townsend
Timberlake Wertenbaker
Victoria Wood

Methuen World Classics

Aeschylus (two volumes)
Jean Anouilh
John Arden (two volumes)
Arden & D'Arcy
Aristophanes (two volumes)
Aristophanes & Menander
Peter Barnes (two volumes)
Brendan Behan
Aphra Behn
Edward Bond (four volumes)
Bertolt Brecht
  (four volumes)
Howard Brenton
  (two volumes)
Büchner
Bulgakov
Calderón
Anton Chekhov
Caryl Churchill
  (two volumes)
Noël Coward (five volumes)
Sarah Daniels (two volumes)
Eduardo De Filippo
David Edgar (three volumes)
Euripides (three volumes)
Dario Fo (two volumes)
Michael Frayn (two volumes)
Max Frisch
Gorky
Harley Granville Barker
  (two volumes)
Henrik Ibsen (six volumes)

Lorca (three volumes)
David Mamet
Marivaux
Mustapha Matura
David Mercer
  (two volumes)
Arthur Miller
  (four volumes)
Anthony Minghella
Molière
Tom Murphy
  (three volumes)
Peter Nichols
  (two volumes)
Clifford Odets
Joe Orton
Louise Page
A. W. Pinero
Luigi Pirandello
Stephen Poliakoff
  (two volumes)
Terence Rattigan
Ntozake Shange
Sophocles (two volumes)
Wole Soyinka
David Storey (two volumes)
August Strindberg
  (three volumes)
J. M. Synge
Ramón del Valle-Inclán
Frank Wedekind
Oscar Wilde

Methuen New Theatrescripts

include work by

April de Angelis
Iraj Jannatie Ataie
Harwant Bains
Sebastian Barry
Simone de Beauvoir/
    Diana Quick
Paul Boakye
Richard Cameron
Fred D'Aguiar
Rod Dungate
Marieluise Fleisser/
    Tinch Minter
Nikolai Gogol/Adrian Mitchell
Bonnie Greer
Noël Greig
Jonathan Harvey
Robert Holman
Kevin Hood
Karen Hope
Declan Hughes
Tunde Ikoli

Elfriede Jelinek/Tinch Minter
Judith Johnson
Manfred Karge/Tinch Minter &
    Anthony Vivis
Barrie Keeffe
Thomas Kilroy
Maureen Lawrence
Claire Luckham
Anthony Minghella
Phyllis Nagy
Winsome Pinnock
Joe Pintauro
Philip Ridley
Rob Ritchie
Diane Samuels
David Spencer
Edward Thomas
Michael Wilcox
Nicholas Wright
Rod Wooden
Sheila Yeger

Methuen Young Drama

Methuen Audition Books and Monologues

Annika Bluhm (ed) *The Methuen Audition Book for Men*
The Methuen Audition Book for Women

Michael Earley and
Philippa Keil (eds) *The Classical Monologue – Men*
The Classical Monologue – Women
The Contemporary Monologue – Men
The Contemporary Monologue – Women
The Modern Monologue – Men
The Modern Monologue – Women

Anne Harvey (ed) *The Methuen Audition Book for Young Actors*
The Methuen Book of Duologues for Young Actors